Her upbringing led Lisa W.B. to become resourceful at a young age. She became very competitive and endured many challenges. Nowadays, she is happily settled in the countryside, surrounded by a loving family.

BASED ON A TRUE STORY

A Fine Line
A BALANCE TO SURVIVE

Lisa W.B

Matador
5 Weir Road
Kibworth Beauchamp
Leicester LE8 0LQ, UK
Tel: (+44) 116 279 2299
Fax: 0116 279 2277
Email: books@troubador.co.uk
Web: www.troubador.co.uk/matador

ISBN 978 1848761 544

British Library Cataloguing in Publication Data.
A catalogue record for this book is available from the British Library.

Typeset in 12pt Perpetua by Troubador Publishing Ltd, Leicester, UK
Printed and bound in Great Britain by TJ International Ltd, Padstow, Cornwall

Matador is an imprint of Troubador Publishing Ltd

I would like to dedicate this book to my loving husband and children, my Mum, who I love dearly, and friends and family who have stuck with me through thick and thin.

I would also like to dedicate this book to my consultant who is a very special person, and without his help and professionalism, I probably would not be here.

INTRODUCTION

This book was driven by a deep desire to express my trauma and the diverse issues and problems that can be caused by child abuse.

Many people on both sides of the line, survivors and carer's are taken to their limits by the severity of the harm and consequential actions that may be taken because of child abuse.

One of the most important factors surrounding child abuse is that the child does not recognise or is aware that the abuse is happening. They are groomed into a state where they perceive an unconditional love. The problem being that the love is not love and is certainly not unconditional. Any child is vulnerable and a child that is being abused has this vulnerability increased.

Paedophiles and abusers alike take advantage of this vulnerability and feed off it. Many children that have been abused manage to survive the experience by suppressing the emotions deep down and go into denial.

Unfortunately the nature of the beast is that when the mind feels at the most relaxed and secure, the beast unlashes and rises to the consciousness. As a consequence, a survivor of child abuse may be at the best stage of their life when they suffer flashbacks and trauma.

I was at one of the best stages of my life with a loving husband and two young children when this beast struck. My story is one of survival and also expresses the ambiguous understanding of even some of the most experienced carers.

One of the purposes of this book is to make the public aware that anyone can be subject to a mental illness. I met people from all walks of life and that most people can live a decent life if given the chance and right support. It is only on rare occasions and unfortunate, that these incidents get publicised where mental illness can result in a tragedy.

I would also like to thank the people who gave me the chance to try to unleash my beast and enjoy my life with my family and friends.

I am lucky to have the support of one of the most professional and caring consultants I have come across. In addition I would like to thank his medical team, and all those who have been involved with my care. I am grateful that I managed to have the support of a good nurse, and thank his secretary.

I am lucky to have a brilliant GP and friends who have made me laugh.

I hope to reward my husband and children with a more secure life of love and stability, than we managed in the past.

My message conveyed in this book is to hope that more awareness is brought into the open about mental illnesses and to show that it is not something to hide from, but to be proud to be able to deal with it and move on.

CHAPTER 1

Balance to survive

I considered carefully how I was going to continue with my therapy without causing harm to myself or anyone else. My main aim was to get out of this cage, and home to my loving husband and children. My Mum and best friends, had been against me coming in, and I now wondered if they were correct.

Yet, Joseph my husband, and I had followed Dr Lynn's advice and we both believed that for me to get better, we both had to go through this. Joseph had to endure the uncertainty of not knowing how the therapy would affect me. He had the sole responsibility of looking after our young children, his business, and our animals. I felt a huge responsibility of trying to get better as soon as possible and to get home again. I had never been in a psychiatric unit before, and it terrified me. Some of the inpatients were very sick, and it was a shock to be amidst the unpredictable environment.

Now I was seriously thinking, that to get out, I had to work intensively and throw everything on the same plate together and deal with it. I had come into hospital as an inpatient, to deal with posttraumatic stress after years of extreme abuse. I had expected the therapy to last two weeks, as Dr Lynn had promised my family I would be home soon. I never expected the therapy and work to be so intensive and difficult. Now I was so desperate to get out I threw all my energy to demonstrate and try to off load my past.

Dr Lynn told me to be as descriptive as possible and to use anything. Suddenly, as I looked up to the far corner of my room, I could picture a scene of drawing a leg opening from the corner, as if some one was sitting up, with legs stretched wide open. I grabbed a pencil, climbed onto the cupboard top and began to draw. I drew a leg stretching out on to the left wall, as if the centre of the vagina was in the corner, and a leg stretching out onto the right wall. In the centre, where the walls met, I drew explicit detail, thinking I want to go home I can do this. Whilst scribbling, thinking how to illustrate blood around the opening and all the bruising. I glanced across to where my plate of toast lay, there was an unopened jam. I rushed out, shutting the door and went into the ward kitchen. Grabbing a plate, I placed bread, and a handful of assorted little plastic tubs of jam, strawberry, raspberry, and blackcurrant on to it.

In my mind, the lighter blood could be the raspberry, where it had darkened was the strawberry, and where it had congealed, and gone thick was the blackcurrant. The creativity completely took over. I used the blackcurrant where I knew the blood would be thick and dark, and enhanced it with the others. This inspired me, as it looked realistic, the jam making it three-dimensional. It also brought home the horrors I had endured, and I quickly drew the man's car cigarette lighter, whirling the pencil, creating the inner coils. Then I coloured it with the strawberry jam to make it red hot, drawing z's from it indicating the heat.

Over the sink was a wide space, and I used it to demonstrate the knife the man used, not big but effective, using raspberry jam on the sharp end. I was well pleased, as my drawings to me, could not have been more realistic of the past. I could see the knife just edging out his pocket, it was ironic it was a Swiss one.

I was now married to a Swiss man who was lovely. I continued to draw from my memories. A corded patterned rope, a cross representing the many times I did not think I would live, pausing, I then drew a cloud of blackness and some child's feet coming out with two big adult ones above and in between them. The contrast of the small feet to the big was making my heart lurch at the vulnerability.

Behind the door, I quickly drew my safety get away, my tranquil quarry, and trees, having no turquoise; I relied on the pencil to make it real. I wrote RIP on the cross, reminding me of my little baby cousin who had died so tragically and I drew a small child's coffin for him.

Lying back on the hospital bed looking up at the legs in the corner, I thought I could not be more descriptive. Then I caught sight of my dressing gown belt, and had another idea. I formed a noose with it, and hung it from the ceiling. He had used it around my neck.

I now had used as much creativity as I could to express the horrors, without passing out or shaking. I put it down to concentrating on completing a work of art, rather than the reality of it all. As I looked at it, I did not see the horror it truly represented. I saw a piece of work that I had managed to do, to fulfil Dr Lynn's wishes.

The door opened and Abdul, a Muslim male nurse came in. He was always lovely, and had come to say hello. He took one look at my room, and ran out, then nurse after nurse were popping their heads through the door. I lay on my bed, thinking I had done a good job for Dr Lynn, but was now getting worried about the reaction it was causing. Ruth the staff nurse came in.

"Oh my God, Bridget," she pulled down the noose I had made with my dressing gown belt. "Dr Lynn told me to be as expressive as possible and to use anything," I muttered.

Ruth sounded cross, "Well I'm sure he didn't mean putting jam on the wall or making a mess. How will we get it off?"

"It will wash off easy. I'd never put anything on that was permanent," I felt offended. "Right, you're to stay in your room," she looked at me frowning. "Can you fetch Dr Lynn?" I asked, wanting him to see it, eager to go home and do whatever he said to get home. "No, I can't, he's not in today, but his junior Dr can come and sort this out," Ruth stormed out. I sat on the bed dismayed. Abdul came in, "What were you thinking of?" he asked, looking at me, avoiding looking up, "How can you let your kids into here?"

"Don't be silly," I said crossly. "I'll have washed it off by then; I was only doing what was asked," I felt annoyed, thinking I had done really well and was just getting grief for it.

The younger Dr was horrified. He completely brushed aside my explanation, and told me to get it off as quickly as possible. He did not take into account that I knew my kids would not be in for days, or that I was just trying to please Dr Lynn. He saw it as a sick pornographic scene, of destructible nature.

When he went out, I grabbed a cloth, soap, and washing bowl, and started to clean it up. An hour later, the walls looked better then they had done before.

The next day was ward round, and without warning, Dr Lynn came into my room, followed by Andrea, and Ruth. I reacted remarkably fast and bolted through the door. Andrea made a grab missing me; I flew out the double doors, and bolted up some stairs. I had no idea where I was going, but after running up the first flight, saw some slatted windowpanes, an easy way out. I jumped onto the ledge smashing through the slats with my feet and hands. Bending to jump, I realised the roof opposite was quite a few feet away, and there was a huge drop in between. Every feeling in my body screamed at me to escape. I jumped; simultaneously someone grabbed my ankle, pulling me heavily back in, on top of people.

They carried me struggling back to my room, telling me to sit down. Panting and out of breath, I looked up, there was a crowd of nurses outside my door, and then Ruth came in. She told them they could go back. "What are we going to do with you? You know Dr Lynn, Andrea, and me." I shrugged my shoulders. All I knew was that without warning, I was terrified and had tried to get away from the danger, "I'm really sorry, I'll pay for the damage," I was genuinely upset.

"Don't be silly, that is what we have insurance for," Ruth smiled, "but you know what this means don't you?" I shook my head thinking of the damage to the window. "You're back on level one; you're too unpredictable at the moment." Ruth said.

"But, it's only because everyone crowded into my room," I protested.

"Yes, but you could have ran outside through the door, the way most people go," Ruth laughed.

"I didn't have time to plan my route," I was still arguing.

I lost out and had to resign to the fact that I was back on level one. This meant a nurse permanently at shoulders length to me. I thought back to my feelings and earlier conversation with Dr Lynn.

How could I tell my closest friends and family that although I loved them, I experienced great periods of distress where I had to fight to keep alive? Most people with an outside view would tell me to pull myself together and remind me that I had two children. This only added to the guilt. I loved my daughter Jo Jo and son Tee Jay. I would protect them with my life, yet I was unable stop the intensity of the intrusive suicidal thoughts and flashbacks. I could not in my own mind, justify what was going on. All I knew was that at these times although I was suicidal, I was not aiming to kill myself. I was actually fighting with all my resources to stay alive and safe. Dr Lynn and the medical team knew this and I tried my hardest to explain to Joseph my Swiss husband of five years.

I knew if the situation was reversed, I would take it as an insult and think he did not love me enough. I had to cling on to Dr Lynn's words, that I was ill, and it was the illness causing this, it was not my wishes. He said it was way down beyond conscious levels, describing the way we would work together in hospital. Saying it would be like pulling the layers off an onion gently, to get to the heart of it. Joseph liked and respected Dr Lynn, and placed his trust with his medical opinion. I recalled the day I entered the psychiatric unit.

I was apprehensive. I had agreed to go in for two weeks voluntarily, at the beginning of March 2001. I had been an outpatient of Dr Lynn's since 1994. Only after breaking the news to Mum, and knowing Joseph would be able to cope with his wine business, and our children Jo Jo who was four, and Tee Jay who was 2 years old, did I agree to go. The months prior to my planned hospital stay, flew by, and I became increasingly agitated, pacing the rooms of our house unable to settle. It had taken me all my time not to shout at the children. I had gone through intense periods of guilt, cuddling both of them, holding them closely, and telling myself it was only for two weeks.

Then my friend Sandra reminded me how they had forced her Mum to have electroconvulsive therapy. I had seen for myself, her damaged memory. She had to write everything down in note form. I had seen pictures in a medical book of the wires attached and it had scared me. I told myself I was not going in for that, trying to be rational. Sandra still insisted I should not go in to hospital. Mum would not talk about it, and my close friends Susanne and Tom told me not to go.

Joseph told me to ignore them all. He said that they did not know enough detail to judge. Consequently, I packed my bags for hospital. Scared, I had taken off the back of my mobile phone and hidden a couple of razor blades and others in the lining of my different bags. I was not planning to use them but felt comfort in the knowledge of having them there.

The day of my planned hospital stay arrived. Joseph and I walked into the hospital together through the double doors to the ward. A nurse had informed us that Andrea, who was my community psychiatric nurse, was on her way, and showed us to the communal lounge. It freaked me out looking at the surroundings, and I grabbed Josephs arm, running towards the seated area, where we had first walked in. Joseph turned to face me saying, "You know it's for the best." I looked at his face and searched his eyes. They were full of concern. "I miss the children already, I miss the animals, and I want to go back," I pleaded.

"Please wait until Andrea gets here, please," he begged, gripping my arm tightly. Just at that moment Andrea came. She saw me with my bags, and looked at Joseph. He said, *"She doesn't want to stay."*

"Oh why not, Dr Lynn will be down in a minute, and I have your own room for you," Andrea replied smiling.

"I think it panicked her when they told us to go into the lounge," Joseph said. I nodded.

Andrea spoke. *"I've your own room and once we explain to the nurses, you won't have to go into the lounge, please, come and look,"* she beckoned to both of us. I nervously followed her back along the ward, to a small room with a bed, sink, and wardrobe. Glancing through the sealed window, I felt like an animal trapped in a cage. Joseph followed, placing my bag down on the disinfected floor. A nurse came in to take it, and I was just going to object when Andrea intervened stopping her.

Inside my head, I thought, I have to do this for Joseph and the children. Yet every instinct screamed for me to run out. Joseph hovered anxiously, until Andrea turned to him, *"Look, I won't leave her, and Dr Lynn will be here shortly."*

I nodded, smiling falsely, *"It's ok you can go,"* I could not look at him as I spoke. We had previously agreed he would not visit me later, as the children would need him, our animals would need looking after, and he would have his business to run. He hugged me tightly, and for a second I clung to him. *"Don't do anything silly,"* he whispered.

"Go," I said whilst I could still speak. He left the room.

"I don't know if I can do this," I said to Andrea, sinking onto the bed.

"You'll be busy. The time will pass quickly, I know the surroundings aren't brilliant, but you need to be here. We had come to a standstill."

The tall sleek figure of Dr Lynn lumbered through the door. They both sat down. *"Not quite home from home is it?"* Dr Lynn said, apologizing.

"But you're only here a short while, and I want you to work hard," he smiled across at me. I felt a tiny bit of reassurance that it may be ok.

He leaned across showing me his paper. He had drawn a long line. One end he had written A, the other end B. *"A is where you were born; B is where we are* now. Between these I want you to write down any significant event that's important to you," he instructed.

I nodded. It gave me something to concentrate on and work at. He continued to tell me some of the procedures and told me that one of the nurses would be my key worker, and I was to go and ask if I was not sure about anything. "Right, I'll see you tomorrow," he left the room. Andrea said, "Don't worry, I'll try and see you every day."

"Thanks," I smiled, as she left.

I now felt alone and looked round. The walls marked and scuffed. The floor looked reasonably clean. I started to sort through my bag, and then I did not want to, I wanted everything together, in case I needed to go. The smell from the elderly dormitory opposite was strong, reminding me of when I sat near my elderly Grandpa as a child.

A voice suddenly started to shout, "Nurse, nurse," and I heard the footsteps of a nurse going through to the dormitory. Two nurses were trying to calm an elderly woman down. I crept back to my bed and someone looked through the glass panel and went. I felt scared, lost and my privacy invaded.

I suddenly needed to hide, desperate for space alone, I climbed into the wardrobe, squatting down, pulling the door shut. It was dark. I felt safe. My mind was racing. Do I run? Do I stay? What was I going to do? I heard the voices of some of the patients. I felt stifled in the wardrobe. I tried to think rationally and thought of meditation and yoga. I desperately tried to do some deep breathing to relax.

In the background, I heard the door open to my room and the nurses asking where I was. Then the door shut and they went out. A few minutes later, they were back, and I heard someone say I had not left the ward. The door opened and a blinding light hit me in the face, I blinked not able to see. "What are you doing in there?" Stepping back, she continued gently, "It's ok we're not going to hurt you." I was shaking from head to foot, unable to move, reminding me of when he approached me in the safe. I jumped as the nurse in front of me, tried to touch my arm. She then turned to the two other nurses. "It's ok you go, I'll manage."

It was only her and me. I scrutinized her long brown hair scruffily falling over her face, covering her oval rimmed glasses. She smiled, genuinely looking *concerned. I let her half help me out of the wardrobe, falling with cramp. She helped me on to my bed. "My name's Anna, I don't want to scare you, have you had a drink since you've been here?"*

I shook my head and she went to the door and called another nurse. "How do you like your tea, or would you prefer coffee?"

I went to answer her but could not speak. I was still shaking and the whole bed rocked.

"Do you like tea strong with sugar?" she asked gently.

I nodded, curling into a ball for protection, staring at the wall wishing none of this were happening. I felt her sit down on the bed. Another nurse approached, and I jumped so hard, Anna jumped, and the other nurse gave a small yelp. Anna said to her, "She was in the bottom of the wardrobe." I could not see their glances and Anna stood up, "I'll see you later, this is Ruth your key worker, she also happens to be one of the top nurses here. She'll look after you." I was still shaking, feeling the bed go again, as Ruth sat down. She put her hand on to my shoulder and I flinched. "I can see Brenda coming in with your tea, wait a minute. I'll fetch it." I heard her shut the door, hearing the clunk of the mug as she put the tea down. She approached me slowly, half propping me up as she shook the pillows, and turned the top one vertically to give me more support. I looked at her, feeling embarrassed. She gave me a lovely beam, her eyes were so dark, and soft, I liked her immediately. She was small and had blonde hair. Ruth told me about the procedure for meals. The fear in my face must have been apparent.

"I'll make a note that you can eat in your room," she said.

Later, she showed me the kitchen. I followed her up the corridor, terrified, yet the toilets were along this narrow bit, so I needed to find them. Ruth was kind. She and Anna made a curtain in my room over the glass panel with a towel, so I had a bit of privacy. I had to leave a tiny gap, as they had to monitor me. They promised it was just a quick glance to know I was ok now and again. They also agreed with Dr Lynn, that I could sit at the desk in the reception, which was normally strictly for nurses.

That evening I decided to take up the offer of sitting at the reception desk. I had talked to Joseph on the phone and the children, assuring him I was ok. It was nine thirty and an older nurse sat at the desk, the younger nurse had disappeared to the nurses' station with a message. I pulled my chair up and sat at the end of the desk with a drink. There were a couple of people sitting on a sofa and a few mooching back and forth to their respective side wards. The ward was mostly for elderly people, but there were a few young ones there, that saw Dr Lynn. I still felt nervous and eyed the nurses in the nurses' station. The young one came back, smiling at me as she sat down. Suddenly the older nurse shouted. "What the hell do you think you're doing?" She was so loud and rough that I did not dare lift my head up, feeling sorry for the two young lads mucking about under the duty board. Again, she shouted. "I'm talking to you, move."

This time I did look up, and was horrified that she was glaring at me and standing up. Her eyes were bulging with rage, and everyone was staring at me. I bolted back to my room panicking, desperate for a razor blade.

I grabbed one throwing myself on the floor next to the storage heater. I held the blade against my skin drawing blood on my arm. I did not feel it. I just wanted to feel safe and ok again, I missed Joseph and the kids. I repeatedly slashed my arm, the floor turned red. The nice young nurse came in. "Please don't do that," she appealed. I looked up at her. She came nearer. I cut again. She moved to take the blade and then pulled back, as I cut a deeper cut. It shocked me as I could see the white edge of my skin peeling back from the blade. The next thing I knew was the horrible older nurse had come into the room. "You think you're clever, do you know what seclusions like? I bet you do, you'll end up in there."

I had no clue what she meant. She scared me, "I've met your sort before, you won't win this way," her tone was frightening and her eyes still bulged. I cut; I wanted this nightmare to stop. She left the room and I leant against the heater. I stopped cutting, but held my razor tightly. It was my protection if anyone came near me. A young man walked up to me introducing himself as the Dr on duty. "Do you think that's a good idea?" He sounded sarcastic. I stayed silent, and he held out his hand asking for the blade. His eyes met mine and reluctantly I gave it to him, and he disappeared. The nice young nurse came in with some saline solutions and a bandage, and gently cleaned my arm. The panic had diffused and I let her finish, muttering, "Thanks."

Later I crossed the corridor to the toilet; quickly washing making sure the glass panel was covered and got into bed. I could hear an elderly woman shouting. "Nurse," seeming ages before I heard footsteps, and the nurse responding to her call. Another one came and I could hear them trying to lift her out of bed onto a bedpan.

I learnt to listen to the footsteps, eventually identifying each nurse, by the shoes they wore. I tried to put my head under the covers hiding from the torch light, which shone into the room regularly. The blood on the floor reminded me of a hostile environment.

I stood up, enough recalling of my first day and night in hospital. It was a mixed reaction, experiencing empathy from some staff and extreme abuse from others. My level one nurse stood also and she followed me to the toilet, an unfortunate witness, to my necessary toilet requirements.

I walked back to my room. The walls still looked a lot cleaner and I sat down to work and concentrate on my lifeline. I started to fill in my earliest significant memories.

I was born in January 1961 and my earliest memories were of my first day at infant school at the age of five years old. I was in the same class as Susanne, still my best friend now. I made a mark near my date of birth and wrote adopted. My parents thought they could not have children. They adopted Jane in 1958, whose birthday was on the same day as Mums, and then they adopted me in the spring of 1961. Little did they know that Mum would actually bear a child two years later, and in June 1963, my younger sister Denny was born. I scribbled hard, making the mark into a big star so as to belittle the adoption bit.

Most people did not know my sister and I were adopted. Jane looked like Mum as she was part fair, and Denny looked like both my parents having very blonde hair. I was dark haired with dark olive skin. Mum used to joke and say I was the milkman's.

Dad was a true gentleman, believing heavily in his role to provide food on the table, and Mum's role to keep the house in order and to have his meals ready. He was a conservative and freemason, and the household diary ran around his Masonic duties. These were kept confidential, and we were ignorant about the freemasons, except that they raised money for different charities and later at school, we learnt there was a joke about the handshake.

I looked at my lifeline, it looked so bare. I lay back on my propped up pillow and sucked at my pencil, trying hard to think of my childhood.

I was always satisfied to stay at home and play in our large garden, making a den under the huge willow tree, or climbing the old apple tree at the bottom and spying on Dad. I often took the dogs for a walk, or spent hours bird watching. I loved animals, reading all I could about them. My two sisters in contrast spent time watching Top of the Pops and having many friends. Jane loved to read, spending more time in her bedroom with stacks of magazines. Denny was a bit of a tomboy like me. We would play football together in the garden, or see who could climb the highest tree. We had homemade bows using fine green garden sticks as arrows, learning to bend a cane, and with the right twine, sending arrows sharpened with Dad's penknife, to penetrate the old apple tree, and draw the sap. The arrows were lethal, and I actually shot Denny in the leg once. We were so scared at the time that we pulled it out, stuck some ointment on it with a plaster, and told no one. Luckily, for us it did heal ok. I laughed, as I remembered the day clearly.

We also played Jacks, where we stood apart from each other and threw a knife into the ground, and the opponent would have to stretch their foot to where the knife landed, whilst not moving the anchor foot. I sighed; I had loved our garden and dogs and had never really wanted to move out.

I glanced at my lifeline. The two significant marks were adoption and starting school. I did a mark from the age of 5 to 12 with a little smiley face and question mark. I placed my paper down and stood up.

Immediately the nurse stood as well. "Let's go and get a drink," I said.

He followed me closely to the ward kitchen. I made a drink for both of us and headed back to my small room to try to continue with my lifeline.

As I picked it up, I threw it down again frustrated. I felt like a prisoner. What was I doing stuck in a psychiatric unit? Why had I agreed? I still questioned whether I should have agreed to let them section me. At the time, I did not really know what choices I had. It was only after I had been in for a few days.

It was not even nine thirty, bored; I looked round the room to see what I could do. Noticing the steel plates screwed to the doors under the handles. I picked up the knife that came with the toast and used it like a screwdriver. I undid the metal plate carefully keeping everything. Then I turned to the cupboard door and started to take that off. I thought of the light switch but did not want to endanger anyone so I left it alone. Sighing I put the knife down and tried to read a book, but could not concentrate.

In the end, I sat on my bed and left the door open. I could see the nurses changing the beds opposite. The smell of the soiled sheets hung heavily. I remembered Dr Lynn telling me off, which was a shock, over the razor blades. "Do you want me to help you?" he had asked pulling up the chair.

I nodded. "Well where are they?" I had looked at him blankly. "Don't be clever, I'm not letting you stay here, and put others including yourself at risk if you don't hand them over."

Blushing, I knew he meant the razor blades. I got my handbag, taking one and others out my makeup bag. I hesitated, when he asked if there were any more. He had three, "Come on, I wasn't born yesterday where's the others?" I grabbed my mobile phone and pulled the battery cover off. He actually laughed and shook his head. "I can't believe it's your first time in and you're like an old pro," he said. He took them off me and left, leaving me frustrated.

Later on that day, staring at a blank piece of paper I felt very frustrated and trapped. I was too scared to sit out at the desk. I could not relax and read. The more I tried to concentrate and write, the harder it became. I became increasingly agitated. The ward was a gloomy place, some patients would suddenly act out, and the environment around me was as changeable as the seasons and extreme. I felt insecure without my razor blades, and I could not distract myself without my home and family around me. I withdrew and my frustration increased. I started to store any security I could think of, in the trend of cutlery and mugs. I would go for a drink and fetch a clean mug leaving the original one under my sink. I took two knives when I had my toast, and stored one. I became obsessed with storing anything I could use to self-harm. I could not release my feelings and the frustration grew, all contact with home became a front. I tried to support Joseph. I knew he could cope if he thought it was worth the struggle, as I would be better. The last thing I wanted to do was to let him down. I did not feel I could tell Andrea or any of the nurses how bad I was feeling, as I wanted to go home and not be kept in longer.

Eventually that evening I snapped. Using a hidden piece of mug, I sat on my bed discreetly slashing my arm; I still felt trapped and was desperate to get outside into the fresh air. Outwitting my level one nurse, I grabbed a jacket, shut my door, and walked quickly down the corridor. I walked straight past the nurse's desk as if everything was fine, and continued down the corridor. Once through the double doors, I hurried across the reception area and out through to the hospital car park. The cold hit me, yet the fresh air was welcoming. I aimed for the gates, and turned down the road. Looking back, to my horror, one of the male nurses in charge was following me. He quickened his pace and I quickened mine. He was catching up. I ran in front of a car, it missed me, braking hard. He followed me, scared I veered in and out of traffic, and realised I had lost him. My arm was dripping and I stood still feeling frozen, not sure what to do. I walked a while and then returned reluctantly to the ward.

I walked slowly back to my room, peeling my jacket off. Shocked at the state of my arm, I lay on the bed, staring at the ceiling, immediately I was aware of footsteps coming down the corridor, and John the male nurse entered. He sat slowly down on the chair opposite the bed, leaving the door ajar. "Can I clean that arm up?" he asked. I shook my head slowly. He stood up to come and look at my arm and I jumped. He stopped, "Look, I'll call a nurse to make you a drink." I lay back on the bed feeling faint. He must have realised as he shouted after the nurse, "Can you bring the blood pressure machine too?"

Whilst cleaning my arm, he asked me, why I ran off. "I was scared," was all I could say. He did not ask me any more and I finished my sandwich and drank a second mug of tea.

The next day Dr Lynn turned up very early, "Bridget, we need to talk seriously," he pulled up his chair, and started to ask me about the night before. I explained that I never planned it. He asked why I did not go to John when I saw him on the roadside. I spoke, "I was scared."

He patted my arm gently, "It is ok, I am not blaming you, but I need to explain to you what we have to do. Have you heard of being sectioned?" I shook my head. "All it means is that like last night when you ran off, John can't stop you because you are in here voluntarily, do you understand that?" I nodded. He continued, "Well if we section you, then if you run off again, it means we have the right to bring you back." He continued to explain a bit more, and asked how I had cut my arm. I told him truthfully and he asked where the remainder of the mug was. I gave him the towel yet did not comment on the odd pieces elsewhere. He told me he wanted me to see another Dr just for ten minutes, to explain how I cut my arm, and then a social worker for a quick word. I nodded in agreement.

Joseph came in later; he seemed upset at what had happened the night before. I assured him I was ok, but had just panicked at being enclosed, and I was still trying to adjust to the hospital. "Look at it," I told him, gesturing at the whole place with my hands, "It would have an effect on anyone," he agreed. He told me the children were fine.

He promised on Saturday, he would bring the children in. He gave me a huge hug and we just clung to each other. I loved him, yet part of me was putting barriers up to protect him, as well as myself. Joseph was shocked I had been sectioned, yet Dr Lynn assured us it was a temporary measure, whilst we worked hard on my past to keep me safe. We had followed his professional advice all the way, and felt we needed to continue, as my care was in his hands.

CHAPTER 2

Peeling off the Layers

On my lifeline, I added my twenty-first, my wedding day, and the children's birthdays. I thought of when I lost Dad, yet I did not want to be reminded, or of losing my Nan. Nearly losing my life in hospital from an overdose was another memory, but again I preferred not to remember.

I sat back. I could see the nurses changing the beds opposite. The smell of the soiled sheets now seemed the least of my worries.

I looked down the corridor it seemed quiet, so I sat at the desk with the two nurses, and my level one nurse. They were nice to me and chatted about all sorts of things. One of them had to keep getting up to do routine check ups on the patients. The other nurse would monitor who went in and off the ward. Down the corridor behind me opposite my room, the nurses were still busy changing beds and helping some of the patients. Most of them were elderly, it reminded me of when I was younger and gave a hand in an old people's home. Some of them here were real characters, and one old fellow named Fred, threw his tea or coffee, at people he disliked. I kept out of his way, yet he winked at me as he shuffled by, to go to the toilet. I smiled at him, and then looked at my book. I carried my book, yet never read it, needing to keep constant attention observing.

Over the hours, I became aware of regular movements and routines. I spent time at the desk eating my sandwiches, ready to move if necessary. I watched Andrea come on to the ward, and speak to the nurses. She started to walk towards my room. I followed her passing the smoke room quickly. She sent my level one nurse away, and we sat and chatted. I felt she was not happy about certain events, but was too professional to make any judgments. She asked me if I had seen Joseph, and I told her that we agreed our priority was the kids, and keeping everything going at home and I rang daily at 4pm to talk to the children.

When she went, bored, I struggled to keep calm. I rang at 4pm and once I knew the children were ok, relaxed a bit. I picked up my lifeline and added starting school, leaving school, the loss of my baby cousin, buying my first house, the births of Jo Jo and Tee Jay, and then losing my Dad.

I knew I had other significant events like meeting my real mum for the first time, staying with my real dad, living with my half brother and sister for a week and them not knowing who I was, and representing my real Mums family at a funeral, having to say I represented the family without revealing who I was. I felt like two people. One who wanted to be at home with the kids and Joseph and be a Mum, and another who was like a petrified child who was going through a living torture.

I decided to have a shower and tidy myself up. The shower consisted of a walk in room with a sink and a curtained shower at the end. A nurse advised me to place a chair, opposite the sink to put my clothes on. The lock was accessible from outside as well. I used flip-flops, hating to walk on the bare floor. My level one nurse stood inside the room, outside the shower curtain. She was useful passing me the towel and clothes. Now dressed, I was staring at myself in the safety mirror above the sink. My dark long hair glistened with the wet, as I ran the comb through it, taking it back off my face. Dark brown eyes, surrounded by shadows, stared back at me, and I headed back to my room.

The next morning I threw the lifeline down in desperation. I spent half the day cursing to myself why I did not get on with it. Always when I tried to remember the past, the blackness would be a key feature. Somehow, it represented extremities, on one side it was a safe feeling and a relief, on the other it felt horrible and scary. I tried to fill in a bit more about the beginning of school. I wrote how I was so shy I did not talk until I was five plus and about meeting Sandra, how she took a special interest, making me feel important.

I wrote how nice it was, being singled out, and to talk about your homework, and how school was. Mum and Dad did ask, but before you could answer, they were back watching the television or reading their book. If you asked a question, they answered in automaton. I could say, "Mum, the house is on fire," I could get back, "Oh yes darling really." They had a talent of conversing, but not really paying attention to what you were saying. In comparison, Sandra asked, "Where's your book? Lets see that drawing, wow that is brilliant etc..."

I wrote in tiny writing, met Sandra, my Mums boss, at the age of twelve. She helped me with my homework. I worked on filling little details in more, and then stopped when there was a knock at my door. Anna entered bringing in another nurse. She was of slender build with brown mousey hair and a wide smile. I liked her straight away. "Meet Alex, she's as mad as me, if not madder," said Anna.

"Right, do you want to eat now, or later?" Alex asked.

"Can we go for a walk? I haven't seen the rest of the hospital yet," I asked.

"Oh, you don't know what you've missed lady," she retorted pulling a face. "No, don't leave your bag there, put it in the bottom of your wardrobe under your dressing gown, I'm not saying anyone will take it, but there are a few confused people here."

I took the message and put my handbag away, discreetly taking a couple of coins out, in case I wanted to go to the restaurant. It was lovely to go outside, and even though it was cold, I loved the fresh air. Alex had also grabbed her coat on the way out.

We headed around the maternity buildings where there were grey squirrels darting back and forth. We came up to the restaurant doors and poked our heads round, one end was busy with people eating their dinners, and the other end had empty seats and a big screen. "We can grab a drink and sit up at that end," said Alex. I nodded, and she showed me how to choose a hot chocolate from the drinks dispenser, saying she would pay as she got discount. I followed her giving her the correct change even when she protested. We sat and watched the news, and I told her, I missed the television. "Haven't you a portable at home?" she asked. I nodded. "Well get Joseph to bring it in."

The next morning Lee, a nurse, came dashing into my room with a file in his arms, "Come on," he said, and opened the door waiting for me to follow him." Come on where?" I asked puzzled.

"Ward round, you have to come in and listen to Dr Lynn and his team."

"Team?" my voice rose in panic.

"Yes, there's him, his junior Dr and Andrea, come on they're waiting." Lee pushed the door wider. I shook my head decisively, I was not being awkward, but there was no way I could enter a room with more than one person, especially with that attention focused on me.

Lee was not sympathetic, "Come on, you're holding them up they have more than you to see." Again, I shook my head, and he stomped off.

Later reading a book, my door suddenly opened, Dr Lynn entered, followed by a stranger and Lee. I bolted charging through them like a cannon ball. A pair of dark brown arms rugby tackled my waist, lifting me off the ground. I turned still trying to run, my legs and arms flailing, desperately scrambling at the wall. In the background, I could hear, "It's alright, it's ok, they aren't going to hurt you," I still ran as fast as I could against the wall, yet I was getting nowhere.

A voice I recognised spoke, "It's ok Bridget, they've gone, there's only me, can we have a chat? Look down at the reception." I turned and gathered myself. I had been trying to run through the side of the wall.

Karen, a West Indian nurse had grabbed me, the stranger and Lee were in reception, and Dr Lynn was beside me. He took my arm gently, "Come on; let's have a chat on our own." I followed him meekly back to my room. He quietly shut the door, beckoning Karen to stay outside and sat on the big leather chair. I fell on the bed. I was still out of breath and in shock. Dr Lynn picked up the paper I had been working on, "Good girl, I see you've managed to add a bit more," he spoke quietly and calmly, and appeared unruffled at the earlier outbreak. "Don't worry, especially about Lee, his bark is worse than his bite." I tried to smile, I felt mixed up.

"I'm genuinely sorry we scared you, I shall make sure it doesn't happen again," he looked at me, and I could see a genuine depth of concern in his eyes. "Look, I know this is more difficult for you then either of us realised, and to be honest may take longer then I initially thought," he hesitated, "We must keep going and you must work hard at it, I want to help you, and we'll get you better, do you believe that?" I nodded, feeling as if I wanted to hug him. He was so kind and caring. "Look Bridget, Andrea was supposed to come in, but she was at the ward round, I do have to discuss what's best for you with my team. I hope you understand that. I will now send her in this afternoon. We do care about you, and want to get you home as soon as possible."

I took my chance, "Can I go home for the weekend?" he shook his head slowly. "Do you know why?" he asked me.

"I guess you want me to concentrate, and not be diverted off track," I said disappointedly looking down at the floor. "Yes, you guessed right. Joseph can bring the children in, and don't worry I do want you to go home to them," he continued. "If you find this lifeline hard, then also draw, write, and illustrate anything you get into your head. I know it's difficult and I've seen the drawing Ruth took, believe me it's better it all comes out, then we can see where we're going, I'll see you tomorrow, and Andrea will see you this afternoon," he got up and left the room.

I felt alone and despondent, yet Karen came in to tell me the dinner trolley was there. Again, she asked someone to get me some sandwiches and a pudding. I hoped at the weekend Joseph would be able to get me something better. The steamed vegetable smell, with the odd aroma of fish or meat made me feel sick. The only good thing was the blackcurrant cheesecakes, the digestive at the bottom was crunchy and buttery, and the acidity of the blackcurrant bit into the creamy flavour of the cheesecake. The nurses had been kind and looked for one for me, each time the trolley came.

Andrea came and made a joke about Lee not being that bad, or the Junior Dr. I laughed, as I could see the funny side, although I did not think it was funny earlier. She also told me she would ring Joseph, explaining to him why they did not want me to go home.

Days past, and I learnt that after they had given me my dinner in my room, it was up to me to put it back. When I put the empty tray and plate back on the stand next to the lounge door, I missed off the stainless steel cutlery. Yesterday I found out by accident, how quickly a spoon, knife, or fork could break. I was lying on my bed bored, I tried it out of curiosity, and to my surprise, the teaspoon snapped, and where the breaking point was, it was not only sharp, but also hot. My curiosity stretched further and I found that a knife could snap in two, within a couple of seconds. The fork would break just under the head where it was at its narrowest. This became a habit and I learnt to hold any of them behind my back and snap it at first attempt. I felt comforted, it gave me the feeling I was still in control, especially as I was able to take it and store it in my drawer. I found the knives useful to take things apart in my room. I still had some mug pieces, which lay untouched in several areas.

This afternoon Ruth was in charge, and I had seen her once when she passed my room, and waved whilst I was waiting for Andrea. Now I plucked up courage, went, and knocked on the nurses' station. Ruth came to the door. "Can I see you later, if you get a chance?" I asked. She nodded. Happier I went back to my room.

I started to work on what Dr Lynn had asked me to do, and ended up drawing a deep pit with me at the bottom, and a bigger person looking down. Further along I drew the quarry and filled it in black, with plenty of trees around making it feel safe. I drew the rope I could see in my head, and tried to concentrate on the pattern of the cords wrapped together. I then coiled it round and round like a snake. I could see the dagger and coloured in the tip as if it had cut me, with blood on the end. Last, I drew a coffin and a cross remembering the trapped feeling.

The pain of cutting, always took the distress away. It was minimal to the feeling of darkness, from not being able to escape. I started to make everything that could be dark, as black as possible pushing all my weight on the pencil, until my fingers were black from the smudges.

All I had done was draw a picture, yet I felt scared and bad. Looking at the black on my fingers, and on my picture made me remember when I passed out everyday, from the weight on top of me. I suddenly could not breathe and ran out of my room crashing into the wall of the corridor and the blackness came. I heard running footsteps, a voice in the background was saying. "Bridget, Bridget, open your eyes." I was unable to move, or acknowledge the voice. It was a few seconds later, I focussed staring at somebody's kneecap. I tried to sit up, and fell back. John and Ruth supported me into my room, and on to my bed. "What happened?" Ruth asked, and then she saw the sheet of paper on my bed. "Right, I'll take that, you for now need a rest."

I sighed, I did not want to rest, "Please can Joseph bring my TV in?" I asked. Ruth hesitated, "Only on one condition."

"What's that?"

"You let me watch it with you sometimes."

I laughed and nodded. "Well if it passes the safety checks then yes."

"Thanks." I rested on the bed watching the time, as I wanted to ring home at four o'clock. When I did, Jo Jo answered, "Hello Mummy."

"Hello darling and how's my big girl?" I asked, longing to cuddle her.

"Fine,"

"And how's Tee Jay?"

"He's in trouble; today he spilt all the milk over the breakfast table and Daddy's letters."

"Oh dear, did Daddy tell him off?"

"Yes because he said one of the letters was a kek."

I laughed, "You mean cheque, never mind, I bet you've been a good girl."

"Mmmmm," I could imagine her nodding her head down the line.

"Have you got anything else to tell me?"

"I love you Mummy."

"I love you too darling, I'll talk to you tomorrow, is Tee Jay there?"

"Mmmmm," then there was a lot of clicking, and she was shouting for her brother to come. Tee Jay came and answered the telephone. "La la," he said. "Hello darling, it's Mummy, I love you, and I hope you're being a good boy, is your Daddy there?" I knew Joseph would be holding him and listening, and he came on the phone. "Love you," I said.

"Love you too, how are you doing?" he asked.

"Ok, but it is horrible, I get so bored, please bring the television," I was begging down the phone. He agreed to, at the weekend.

The nurses were making the bed in the next room, and I wondered who was going to occupy it. I soon discovered a girl of about the same age as me, had moved in. Every time I passed her room, she was sitting on the floor crying. I felt bad and was not sure whether to talk to her. It was about an hour later, when I was returning to my room from the kitchen, that I heard a big smash come from her room. Then another and it was so disruptive, it made me jump and I got the shakes. I sat on my bed sipping my tea. I heard the nurses go running in there, and an argument broke out. It turned nasty and there was a lot of swearing. I tried to ignore it.

CHAPTER 3

Trapped

The two weeks voluntary came and went, and it was with bleak realisation I was trapped, requests for weekend breaks refused. Joseph and I learnt the hard way, that sectioning meant I was powerless, and relied on the authority of Dr Lynn, for every movement.

This had a rebellious effect on me, and I would look for any opportunity to prove to myself, that I was still in control. I would search for out of bound items and purposely hoard them. I would escape any chance I got, and besides bolting impulsively due to my illness, I started to plan and look for opportunities to get outside. I also started to build relationships with other patients on the ward.

For the next few weeks, I continued to talk to Dr Lynn. He tried many different approaches, the kind one, and the one where he entered the room swearing, which really worked me up. He used different tactics, and I tried many back. One day fed up on level one, I made an excuse that I needed to come with him, to talk to someone at the station, and as he entered the nurses' station, I bolted down the corridor. Another time, I pinned him up against the wall saying, "If I can't go home, you can't," I was five feet two and he six foot seven, so I was standing on tiptoes, and he was laughing. He could see the funny side, at the time I was serious. He was good to me, and broke the rules, and although I was on level one, he let me out of the building. It was only, when enclosed that I was bad. Several times, when he saw me in my room, I would blockade the exit, pleading with him to let me go home. He hated me doing it, but I really needed my kids. He never agreed.

It was approaching June. I was depressed and wanting to go out. The sun shone, and I felt like a budgerigar sitting in a cage, in front of the window watching the world pass by. What made it worse would be comments that I had to endure like the budgie. It was not, "Who's a pretty budgie then?" A stupid phrase because the poor bird would not care if it were pretty or not stuck on its own in a cage. I got remarks like, "Aren't you missing your children? Don't you want to go home?" of course, I was missing my children, and of course, I wanted to go home.

I still rang home everyday, and when Joseph and the children came, I would go outside in the grounds with them. Sometimes I had a level one nurse with me, other times we were on our own. Tee Jay used to play with the nurses, and Jo Jo would run round like a little princess in a pretty outfit.

Every visit Jo Jo would have made me a picture, which I put up in my room. They were cute, but also represented a little child missing their Mummy. She drew pictures of hearts and of us all, playing together, and always wrote love on every one of them. I used to stare at them, when I was on my own, fingering them lightly, every touch reminding me how much I missed my family.

I worked on my lifeline filling in more detail. Dr Lynn told me to try to start with the least painful experiences, and that we would work backwards. My problem was that we both had completely different perspectives, and concepts of the experiences, and would have many disagreements ending up with Dr Lynn saying I was in denial. I understood why he addressed the problem as he did. Yet my argument was that he was seeing it from his point of view, and not accepting that I had different opinions and ideas through my experience. I was also very much against the concept of labelling and generalising. He would mention, he had seen a great deal of patients with similar experiences, and would generalise. My vision was that everyone was unique and whilst one person may react one way, it did not mean everyone else would. Dr Lynn argued that he did not like labels, and I actually did find him a lot fairer then some of the stories and treatments I had seen other patients receive.

I stared at my lifeline now and looked at the dates and names on it, as I scrutinised it, looking for a place to start. I remembered when I had first met Dr Lynn.

It was Monday morning, Joseph was at work, and I had my first hospital appointment with Dr Lynn. I sat in the waiting room with my back to the wall. Luckily, there were not many people in there. A tall man came striding across, from one of the side rooms. He beckoned to the girl near me. He had a nice face, and was younger than I thought. When Dr Pagely had said top man, I had visualised an older person.

It was a quarter of an hour later, when the girl came out of the room dabbing her eyes with a hanky, I felt for her, as in my world people did not get upset in front of others. The tall man followed her out, the jacket of his suit flapping, as he headed for the reception. This time he took another file, "Bridget?" he asked.

Before I could even acknowledge him, he was disappearing into the room. I followed cautiously; he was standing there, holding the door, pointing to a chair. I felt he was studying me as much as I was him. I looked around the room taking everything in. He sat there quietly. If he expected me to say something, he was mistaken. Eventually, he opened the file, glanced at the first page, closed it, and said, "How are you doing?" he crossed his legs leaning forward on the desk. "Fine," I muttered.

He asked me some general questions, and I nodded when I could or shook my head. I was still in awe of him, he was younger than I had imagined, and quite good looking, having dark brown eyes that most people would fall for, and an attractive moustache. Although he looked nice, I was not going to be falling at his feet or trusting him, especially the way the previous occupant had come out crying. He was assertive, yet gentle with his questions; I was not sure what he expected from me. I had come in thinking he would discharge me. His questions that had been quite general switched slightly to the day of the accident. I said little, and nodded if he was correct. He told me to return in three weeks.

I drove home, realising I had been worried, who the top man was, and what he wanted. I joked to Joseph saying how good looking he was, Joseph laughed he knew I was teasing him. The next few times, followed a similar pattern, Dr Lynn would sit, waiting patiently for me to talk, and I would stare silently at the window. Today he pulled his chair up asking, "Why are you here? Why did you ask to see me?"

"Dr Pagely asked me if I wanted to see you or your Junior Dr," I replied hoping he would explain.

"Yes, but why have you come here? Why did you see Dr Pagely in the first place?" leaning forward, he looked intently at me. Uncomfortably I said, "You know why, Dr Pagely must have explained, you have it in the file."

He again looked at me as if to draw the answer from me, "Yes, I do, but I want you to explain and give me your version."

I questioned in my head, why was I there? Every week, I thought he would discharge me, every time he asked to see me again.

"I didn't ask to see anyone in the first place, I was made to see Dr Pagely when I was brought in to the hospital," I said. Dr Lynn looked at me and leant back waiting for me to continue.

I sat on my bed and reflected about Dr Lynn, he was very patient, and I had felt no choice but to tell him about the car accident, the reason I ended up in the psychiatric department. I did not want to discuss it but he was pushing me quite hard.

"The first time I was brought in was because of the accident, the car accident." Dr Lynn still kept quiet and I carried on.

"Richard my brother-in-law, said he had a job for me to do straight away.

He told me to take the other car and deliver the accounts to the accountant in Hinckley, via the motorway.

I grabbed the accounts, got into the other car, had driven a mile or so, when I had a mental block, was Hinckley on the M1 or the M69? I made a quick decision to follow an alternative route.

A few miles up the dual carriageway in my mirror, I noticed a saloon car overtaking other cars coming up behind me. There was no way I could let him pass with the unpredictable bends. I carried on at the same pace, worried, suddenly my car's power cut, the driver behind, went straight into the back of me. The crunch and impact forcing my body and head forward, and then I fell back. My first reaction was to get out of the car quickly to see him. He was a young driver and panicking, some woman shouted from across the road. "Are you alright?" I nodded at her and continued to the car behind. The driver beckoned me to sit in his passenger seat. My legs were going to give way, and I had a funny feeling up my back, I could not feel anything. He rang for an ambulance, and called Richard. I eventually left the hospital with severe whiplash.

When the police came to my house later that day, they said I was lucky, because if I had been on my planned route of the motorway, I could have been killed and others with me. After the police had gone, Richard visited me, and asked if I was ok. When he was going, he shouted to me, "Remember, what I said. If I can't have you, no one else will," he laughed. "What do you mean?" I shouted feeling sick. Suddenly I could not speak. I looked down at the floor. Dr Lynn said, "Try to explain, what your brother-in-law meant?"

"He shouted out, "It's amazing what a bit of dirt in the carburettor will do."

I went inside and locked my door." I took another deep breath and looked at the floor. It was not a nice feeling telling someone that your own brother-in-law had tried to kill you. Dr Lynn had leaned back, stretching his long legs, he was amazingly calm. He had asked, "Do you believe, he meant to kill you?"

I looked at the floor, it led to many other issues, some very private ones.

I sat on my bed, and put the television on. I was only half watching. My level one nurse was changing, and the early shift was going home. An agent nurse took over, and I inwardly grimaced. Sometimes, they were lovely, and at other times, were so inexperienced, and ignorant that they were a potential danger.

Today I had a nurse who was either African or West Indian, and although she was very pleasant and well intentioned, she upset me. She asked if the photographs of Tee Jay and Jo Jo were my children, complimenting them. Pleased, I thanked her and then she started to tell me not to worry, that Jesus would forgive me for being a bad Mum, "He knows," she said gesturing, "You need to pray to the good lord for forgiveness, otherwise you'll end up down there," her eyes looked to the ground. "How many times do you go to church?" was her next question. I did not answer her, feeling guilty. "You need to go home, you shouldn't be here, think of your children, not yourself," she smiled blatantly at me, and I wanted to scream to her, that I had never wanted to come in the first place. It was because I loved my children, that I was doing my best to get well. I stared at her and then another agency nurse entered the room. It was her turn to take over. The first nurse turned to her friend, "I was just telling her to pray to the lord, and he will forgive her for sinning. If she prays he will help her to become a good Mother." The second nurse nodded smiling at me,

"Yes she is right, don't worry, the lord forgives, he won't let the devil get to you, and if he already has, he will help drive him out. Just pray for forgiveness," she turned to her friend and they started to chat.

I sat on my bed, my hand slipping under my pillow to a snapped knife end. I used my fingers to push it up my sleeve, and then pulled it against my wrist. Feeling the wet on my fingers, I knew I had cut, and I felt the relief of taking away some of the pain and guilt, they had thrust at me. I felt unsafe and I walked slowly past them out of my room. They followed me having no idea I had cut, and I walked quickly up to Gill, who had been the nurse, who had once shouted at me to move from the desk.

Since that episode, she had been ok with me. I walked up to her quickly, showed her my arm, and walked to the first aid room. She turned to the agency nurses, "It's ok, I am taking over," they shrugged. She pushed me into the first aid room. "What's going on?" she asked, at the same time, getting the bandages out. "They were telling me, I had to pray to the Lord, that I had evil in me, and I was a bad Mum, but the Lord would rescue me." I was upset, but Gill was even more. She stormed out asking one of the regular nurses to take over.

The next day Dr Lynn demanded an enquiry, and the two nurses were banned from working for the trust. This upset me, as I did not want them to lose their jobs, but I later found out they had denied everything, and said I made it up. Luckily, Dr Lynn and the staff knew me better and trusted my version. The agency nurses that had been banned, did more damage, then they would ever have known, as I used and believed their opinion of me as a Mum when I was down, and would often self harm because of it. It seemed easier to give in and believe I was a bad person, than to fight hard and accept the reality of my past.

CHAPTER 4

The Tape

Andrea walked into my room, pulling up a chair; she beckoned the nurse with me to leave. "Right, down to business, we are going to try another approach," I sat up and tried to pay attention.

"If someone is scared of going to the supermarket and has a panic attack, one of the best solutions is to try to get them to face their fear," she paused, looking at me. "It would be reasonable to take them back to the supermarket and face the situation, they might find it difficult at first, but the rational is that each time they faced it, the symptoms would be less until the fear had gone." I nodded, as that made sense, yet I still did not see how that related to me. "Right, I am not going to ask you to repeat the experiences you have had, as they should never have happened in the first place. However, I do want you to try to face up to some of your past and the idea is, the more you listen and talk about it, the less impact it will have," Andrea was studying my face, all the time she was telling me. I hesitated. It scared me, "I would not know where to start," I muttered, facing my hands up.

"Hold on, you haven't heard all of it yet," replied Andrea. I sat back feeling deflated and not at all happy. "What we want you to do, is write about the least serious incidents, the ones that are easiest for you to relate to, and then, you read it out onto tape." I shook my head violently, "I won't read out, I hate that sort of thing."

"It's important, it is you reading it and you listening after," said Andrea. "After you have listened to it several times, the impact will be less, and you can move on to the next issues. I am going to bring you a cassette tape recorder, and I expect you to start to write down the incidents first. If you prefer, a nurse can wait outside the room when you are recording. The important thing is that you do not play it back when you are alone; you have to have someone with you. The first few times it will be me, and then one of the nurses," she hesitated, and I grimaced, this sounded hard and I hated reading aloud. Andrea stood up, "Look, I am working on getting you a tape recorder, and you can start by writing about the easiest incidents."

I stood up. "How do I know which are the easiest?" In my mind to do that, I had to think about the incidents and open locked doors. Andrea turned, "Sleep on it, and we will talk it over again tomorrow," smiling, she left.

I sat on my bed trying to recall some of the incidents. How I started to work for my brother-in-law Richard.

I had been on the sick with Meniere's disease, an imbalance of the fluid in the ear causing sickness and immobility due to vertigo. Alongside this, I was recovering from not being able to walk without help for two years due to ME. At the age of 29 years, I had at first refused to accept my Dr's diagnosis. I reluctantly had to believe him, after neurological tests at the hospital. I accepted that I was home with my Mum and Dad, with Jena my Italian Spinone, and my three cats. It was hard moving back and even harder to be stuck like a vegetable in a chair. Watching the television could cause fits of nausea, walking down the drive was like a ten-mile marathon. My movements and life had become very limited. I worked hard at recovery, and after visiting a self-help group for ME, I became very determined I was not going to end up like any of them, where the key words were self-pity. It gave me a kick to fight with every resource available to beat the illness.

My brother-in-law Richard asked if I wanted to give him a hand in the mornings doing some engineering work. I jumped at the chance. I first told Richard I would need a word with my Dr, to see if I was medically up to it. My Dr warned me to take it little by little, and at first, I only did the odd hour or so.

Richard being an engineer had a sub-contract to do some work for a vehicle manufacturer. On my first day, he drove to a small village and on the outskirts drove into a farm, which was letting out units. Here there was a pile of lorry bumpers and all sorts of vehicle components. Some just needed a clean; others needed small improvements. I started to do what Richard asked, and was amazed at how fast the time went by. I was also pleased to come out from the very small dark unit and get into the sunshine. Richard seemed happy and asked if I would be up for some more work, I agreed.

I had been working a while for Richard when we changed to a bigger unit the other side of Leicester, nearer the motorway. Richard also took on some contracts turning bushes for machinery. He had a massive turning lathe. I was lucky because Richard taught me how to weld, turn, do proper panelling, and how to spray paint professionally with a generator and airbrush.

Richard was tall around 6ft, having big mournful looking eyes, brown hair and a dark moustache. He was clever, but a complete rogue. He would never buy a parking ticket, justifying it, by saying that the number of times he was caught having to pay; a penalty was a lot cheaper then paying in the first place. He was a character yet would always help people. He had a rough edge with no frills, but now was very clever and capable of making something of his life. He and Jane seemed to get on well and it was no surprise when Jane told me she was expecting.

The Dr signed me off the sick, months after telling me I would never work again. He was as delighted as I was that I proved him wrong, and gave me a huge hug that day. Richard and I worked well together, and the nature of our work was so precarious that at times, each other's lives, depended on the other. We had a contract with the car manufacturer for factory maintenance. We spent time on the factory roof carrying out repairs, and we continued to rack a huge part of the warehouse out, balanced on beams, a couple of inches wide drilling high up. The screws were self-thread and the actual drill screwed them into the shelving. Once we had put up the shelf, we would have to stand on that one, putting up the next, balancing around 50ft up, with no harness. I never thought of the danger, yet sometimes Richard started larking about high up, and then I would get cross.

Richard started receiving work from various firms. This involved travelling down to Winchester, to do some engineering on site. At first, he went alone, and then he asked me, if I would go. I was reluctant as it involved stopping overnight. Yet he promised me everything was in order. Jane was happy. At the hotel, it would be separate rooms and it was good money.

The nurses were changing duty, and another one came into my room to level one me. I took the chance to go and get a cup of tea, and have a break from my thoughts. I contemplated, and still had doubts whether I would be able to write down what happened. It was even harder to imagine reading about it aloud. I sat back on my bed, and sipping my hot sweet tea continued to remember the activities in Winchester.

Friday morning Richard picked me up. After we had passed Silverstone, we stopped at a small roadside café, ordering two full English breakfasts, bacon, sausage and the egg cooked just right. Soon on our way again, Rich was full of banter, joking about his younger brother and my baby sister Denny. He liked Denny who was now married to Jack and had two sons and a daughter. She was lucky, Jacks parents were pretty well off and the children's education already secure. However, from some of her conversations, it was as if she had to fit in to their way of life with no negotiation for hers.

Later we pulled into Winchester, turning left at the traffic lights towards the hotel. We were early, but they took the luggage for storage, and we set off again. Richard drove off the main road and down a small country lane with hedgerows blooming of wild flowers. He turned into a massive drive way, and we took the left fork away from the house which then led past animals in pens into a big courtyard. Parking outside some offices, a huge bearded man came out, calling

*himself Fred. He was the boss and was very blunt, saying, "Come on gal put the
kettle on whilst we men talk business," pointing to a small room.*

*I followed his instructions, taking in his room with the large oak desk,
wooden plaid walls, and cases of stuffed animals giving the room a rich but
distinctive air. He and Richard went into the adjoining room that had several
girls typing, and a huge aviary with birds. I went into the little room, dismayed
at seeing a washing bowl full of dirty mugs, a kettle, tin of coffee and a bowl of
sugar lumps. Looking for clean mugs in the cupboard, I found some milk instead.
I then knocked, interrupting, asking Fred how he took his coffee, "Black gal, no
sugar, I'm sweet enough," he said, turning to talk to Richard. I made the coffee
and walked back in; the two men took it walking to a huge barn. It was here that
Richard would be carrying out the engineering work. My job was to run errands
and help Richard when necessary. Being busy, the time flew by and Richard
stopped just after 5.30pm. "We'll call it a day," he said.*

I stopped working, deciding to take a break and change my bed. The
nurse accompanied me to the room where the sheets were stored.
Together we examined them, as many had coloured residues left on
them and we took time to find the cleanest bed linen possible. I also
took an extra blanket, as I was always cold. We made my bed together
and I sat down and continued my work.

*Back at the hotel Richard suggested we go out to a local restaurant to eat. I agreed
and arranged to meet him twenty minutes later at reception. I had a quick shower,
blasted my hair with the hairdryer, and with a clean pair of jeans on went down
to the lobby. Richard looked perplexed when he saw me, "Where's your other shoes?"
I looked down puzzled and shrugged my shoulders, "I didn't bring any others."*

*Richard actually gasped, "You're kidding me," he walked towards me, "What
if we go to somewhere nice for dinner; you can't walk into a restaurant with steel
toecaps." I looked at him, I honestly had not thought of any leisure time, I had
kitted myself out for work, that was my life.*

Richard took me to the side of the lobby, "Look Bridge, we can't go out like this, some of the shops stay open late in the mall, how about we kit you out?" I looked up at him, he was not laughing, and he was being serious. I felt bad, as I had not wanted to cause any problems. "Ok," I said, and we went out into the street to walk towards the mall. Richard took over, I had no clue what to get, and fashion was not my thing. He first took me into a shoe shop picking a few designs of shoes, and short ankle boots. After I had tried them all on, Richard picked the boots insisting he was paying for the clothing and shoes, as it was his idea. In the next shop was some real modern clothing, and he picked a tight slim top which had beading down it and a zip which could be lowered to look sexy, or kept up looking classy. I was looking at the trousers, but he went and picked a short black pencil skirt with a slit at the front, some stockings, and a suspender belt. I was now, far too embarrassed to say anything, especially as he had already handed them over to the shop assistant. It was easier to smile as if confident with his choice.

Going back to the hotel, I nearly ran to keep up with Richard, he was striding fast and purposeful. In the lobby, he passed the huge carrier bag to me, "Ten minutes max, I'll wait for you here," I took the bag off him and headed upstairs. I felt nervous, I did not do dressing up, hardly ever wearing skirts, let alone stockings, I had no idea how you even fastened them onto the suspender belt.

When I eventually succeeded, I was late, and rushed putting on the tight top. I zipped it down a little, being very modest with it. I then put on the skirt and boots. I received a shock, when I looked in the mirror. I looked so different. The dark brown eye make up and dark mascara enhanced my long eyelashes. My hair shone and the outfit showed off my trim figure, self consciously I walked slowly down to the lobby. Richard sat in the corner waiting. He stood up as I walked towards him, looking like a Cheshire cat, he grinned from ear to ear. "Wow," he said, "That's one of the best investments I have ever made."

I half laughed, feeling nervous and awkward yet part of me felt a little excited. "Let's have a drink here first," said Richard, and he guided me down the stairs to the gallery. Here it was subdued lighting with walnut tables and chairs, there was only another couple in the corner, and Richard went to the bar bringing back the drinks.

Conscious of my short skirt and thighs revealed in the extremely fine shiny stockings, I crossed my legs defensively. Relax I told myself. Richard was in a great mood and he passed my wine and sipped his beer, "You look fantastic, you must know it," he was looking at me and grinning again.

"I prefer my jeans and t-shirt," I grabbed my drink and took a big swallow.

"You need educating," he said. "You need to get out more Bridge, look at you, she's done you no good, I don't know why you stick with her, and she uses you." I knew he meant Sandra, I had to defend her, and I looked at him directly in the eyes, "She's ok, she did a lot for me, it was my idea to have the shop, and I was the one who got ill."

"Yes but why, because you were doing all the work, every time I came into the shop, she was at the back having a fag and you, either serving or carrying heavy plants about, you're much better off without her."

I looked at him, "Well, I don't see her so much now, I have broken away from her and Mum and Dad a bit."

"I know and you've got a nice house and all your animals, now you need someone to look after you," Richard sighed and put his glass down, "By the way we're going to the Leicester speedway next week, are you going to come with Jane and me?"

"I might," I sipped my glass, "What night is it and are you sure Jane doesn't mind?"

"Course she doesn't. I think it's next Tuesday, ring her up," Richard stood up, he and I had both finished our drinks, "Come on there's a great Italian restaurant just round the corner."

In the lorry the next day on the way home, he was laughing his head off, "You wait til I tell Jane you were going to go to a restaurant in steel shoes and jeans," I laughed. I could see the funny side of it.

The nurse changed and I took another break and made a drink, I sat back on the bed, to continue writing about Richard.

We went to the speedway on Tuesday, Jane was glad of my company, for Richard took his brother and his Dad, his Dad kept chatting to me telling me Richard had married the wrong sister. I laughed politely, all the time wanting him to get lost. Jane had never liked him much, and now I understood why. I talked to Jane about my work and she seemed happy Richard had taken me on. "He always says how much work you do," she giggled to me, "His Dad doesn't like it because when he takes him to work, he compares what you do to him, you do ten times more," I laughed back and we had a nice sisterly chat about her in-laws. I was also relieved to hear her saying she didn't mind me working for Rich.

The time passed quickly and Richard asked me to go down again to Winchester, I agreed readily as I wanted the cash, and the work was relatively simple. We decided to go the following Friday and Saturday.

We did not check into the hotel straight away but went straight to the farm. Richard had loads of work and wanted to spend as much time as possible there. Fred came out to meet us and said, "Stick kettle on gal," he and Richard walked off, and once again I bit my lip and went into the kitchen. I took the drinks directly down to where we were working. Fred and Richard were shaking hands on a deal. They rescued me, with the three mugs I was carrying. I worked hard and helped Richard to screw these fiddly bits together. I never asked the business of why Fred wanted all this work doing. I was glad when I could get into the sunshine again.

It was after 6pm when we eventually arrived at the hotel. Richard came out to me in the lobby where I waited for my room keys. "You aren't going to believe this, they only have one room, I definitely asked for two. "I looked at him and could feel the panic rising, "Well we have to go then," I stood up, and Richard put his hand on my shoulder pushing me gently into the seat again, "Look Bridge, it's already getting on for seven we won't get anywhere else near here. We need to finish the job off tomorrow. You will not know I am there; I will even sleep on the floor. Come on, it's not as if I am a stranger, we're family." I hesitated, and he pulled me up, grabbed my luggage as well as his, and started to go upstairs. I had no choice but to follow, not happy, yet he was very persuasive.

I stopped and looked around my room; my level one nurse was reading a newspaper. I was ready to leave the rest until the next day. Then I thought, the sooner I finish, the sooner I get home, and picked my pen up again.

It was a neat twin-bedded room, Richard asked me which bed I wanted, then he went over to the kettle and started to make us both a cup of tea. I relaxed a bit. We decided to go to the Italian restaurant and skip a drink downstairs as it was that bit later. He asked if I wanted a shower first, I suggested that he went first, and then went downstairs and I would join him later. He grinned at me and agreed.

I lay back switched on the TV and tried to listen to the news despite the background noise of the shower. Richard came through with a new shirt and tie and best trousers. He had combed back his wet hair, and I could smell the aftershave. He said, "See you downstairs," and disappeared through the door. I waited a few minutes and then I got up and locked the door. I had the quickest shower, wore my skirt and boots again, and rushed downstairs to see Richard. "Nice outfit," he joked, "I wonder where you got them from?" We both laughed as we went through to the dining area at the Italian.

When we got back to the room, Richard started to make a coffee, and I sat down on my bed. He was the perfect gentleman and put my drink beside my bed before he got on to his own bed to have his coffee.

I sat up and needed to get out of the building, I felt agitated and irritable. The nurse sensed something was wrong and asked me if I was ok. "Fine," I replied, yet I knew I was not as my body had started to shake. I put on my jacket, but my nurse blocked the doorway, "Sorry, you are not allowed out in that state," she said. I stared at her, measuring up my chances if I decided to make a dash for the door. I thought who was on duty and then realised I had no chance, Steve was one of the fastest nurses there. I tried my other option. "Is Ruth or Anna there? Please let me talk to them?"

I was lucky Ruth walked up to my room; she looked at me and raised her eyebrows. I grinned, I knew my arms were shaking, and as much as I tried to stop, could not. "Please," I pleaded, "I'll be better out than locked up," I desperately matched and held her stare, "You know I'll get worse if you keep me in, I promise I'll walk round and straight back," she thought for a moment and looked at her watch. "Tell you what, give me five minutes and I'll take you," I was happy at that and sank back on to the bed with coat on, "Five minutes," Ruth held one hand up, looked at me as if to say don't you dare run for it and walked away. I respected her and the knowledge I could get out helped contain my feelings.

Later crouching on the bed after coming back in, I grabbed my pen. I did not want to think about the incidents and do nothing. If I could write it down at the same time, it would be a step in the right direction.

"Are you ready?" Andrea looked at me waiting for my reply. On the bed was the tape recorder and her finger was poised above the play button. I felt more embarrassed about listening to my own voice then the content.

My voice sounded robotic and dull.

"I was in this hotel, sharing a room because I had trusted him. He was my brother-in-law and had been nice to me. I lay back sipping coffee, so relaxed I did not notice Richard had taken my empty cup and was beside me. When I did, it made me jump, "What are you doing?" I tried to get up; he pulled me down, strong, laughing. Now I felt vulnerable and could feel his hand moving up my thigh."

I sat on the bed mesmerized holding my breath I did not want to hear this. Hands gripping the bed sheets, legs starting to shake. Andrea was staring at me intently.

"His mouth made contact and he was kissing me with force. I tried to take his hand off my thigh, it had reached my suspender belt, and he was undoing the front clips. I could not move my head and his free hand moved over the top of my head and grabbed my arm. He quickly moved it to my other arm, both hands pinned under one of his hands. His leg-straddled mine, pinning it down and his fingers of his free hand, started to stroke under the suspender belt. His whole hand crept underneath. I was still trying to push him off me when my coping

40

mechanism came into force and I was not there. I was on the ceiling looking down. I could see a huge mans body on top, and he was still pinning me down yet he had not penetrated me, he chose to use his hand. Some time later, whether it was hours or seconds, he got off me and lay on his bed. I could still see the other body not moving, lying motionless."

Andrea clicked the button. I looked at her but to my alarm she was fading in the distance and then the black came. I came to on the floor aware of someone taking my pulse. Andrea was looking shocked and helped Ruth put me on the bed. I felt sick and then I realised there were a few people all crowded in my room and I leapt up to bolt out. This time Ruth was quicker, and she and Andrea had both leapt and made a grab for me. I was gasping for air and Ruth asked all the others to leave. I sank onto the bed trembling like an autumn leaf.

"Bridget, Bridge calm down," Ruth patted my shoulder.

Andrea still looked shaken. "Look Bridget, you did well, it will be a lot easier the next time," she placed the tape recorder on the side. My head felt as if it was not there, and when I touched myself I could have been touching cardboard, I did not feel right. As I looked, I had to keep concentrating, one minute it was the hotel room, and then it was mine. I stared at Andrea and Ruth, they were in the room, but as I tried to focus on them, they looked far away in the distance. I felt weird and spaced out. I sat wanting to respond but could not. Andrea was offering me the mug of tea. I stared at the wall. Inside, I wanted to drink the tea or speak, but my body was not connecting to my brain and I felt bad. I could hear Ruth telling Andrea they needed to fetch the Dr, and I heard Andrea say give it a few minutes. I do not know how long passed, but suddenly I was drinking my tea.

It was a few days later when Andrea told me to continue to play the tape. "We should repeat the first bit, but I need to know what's on the rest so if we play it all, and then decide whether we need to cut it or just repeat it," she said. My heart was beating fast and I felt sick I remembered what happened the last time. I sat gripping my pillow leaning back as she pressed the play button.

"Richard put the luggage in the lorry and came back into the hotel to have breakfast. He talked about the night before, telling me, how lucky I was, and that I must have really enjoyed it. I finished my breakfast in silence. On the way back to the farm, he was teasing me again about my shoes. At the farm, we worked quickly wanting to get home, and Fred seemed happy. He showed us round the place. It was huge. Besides the offices, at the back there were tennis courts, a massive swimming pool and a lot of old farm machinery. There was also a sauna cabin and he joked to Richard saying he would have to come and use it.

I was glad to get home hugging both my dogs. My home was my castle and I felt like building a moat around it. I still went to see the Dr regularly, he was glad that I was doing so well. Richard started to get more and more contracts and I was busy. One day I would be doing all the accounts and typing, the next I could be using the forklifts or using the industrial strimmer to do the lawns. I had mixed feelings doing this. I loved cutting the grass and being outside. I hated having to do the slopes, which were quite precarious and led down to the open planned building, built mainly of glass, so everybody could see you. Many of the men took the Mickey out of me, dressed in engineer's overalls, and doing the work, I did. I loved it in the summer, and would chuck the overalls for a pair of shorts and t-shirt. Now I was drilling a hole in the concrete, to put some safety barriers up, for the forklifts, to protect the end of the racking. The reinforced cement needed an extremely heavy hammer drill. It made a noise and I purposefully waited until someone went by and made them jump. Richard was putting the barriers in place and readjusting where necessary, he had made them himself, and now they were painted up and in place, they looked good. I carried on drilling and fixing. We were lucky as the job was straightforward and we finished quickly. We had some more turning to do at the unit, so made our way back. I was due a cheque and asked Richard if I could have my wages, he turned to me joking and said, "What's it worth?" I felt my heart start to beat faster and as I looked towards the door, Richard ran over and turned the key.

"*Don't mess about,*" *I said walking towards the door, he stopped me and grabbed hold of my overalls.* "*Let's see if there is really a woman under there?*" *He was laughing and I tried to stop him, but he was strong and it seemed to encourage him more. He put his hands under my overall and even under my t-shirt, laughing.*"

My voice on the tape was shaky and I took some deep breaths. Andrea pressed the pause button. "Are you okay to continue?" I nodded determined to leave my past behind and get home to my kids. The pause button clicked followed by my voice.

"*I struggled begging him to stop, thinking of Jane, whether I should tell her. His hands now were round my breasts squeezing my nipples and playing with them, suddenly he fumbled, pulling my bra off my arm, down my sleeve laughing. I was trying to grab it back. He threw it at me and walked back to the desk. He got his chequebook out, wrote out a cheque, and gave it to me. I put it into my handbag and now fully dressed I walked outside and waited by the lorry. He dropped me off and we agreed to meet at 6.30am in the morning.*

The tape clicked and I looked up to see Andrea. "How far did it go?" She asked quietly but firmly. I tried to think of the struggle in the unit, and as I tried to answer, the black came releasing me temporarily from the distress of the memory. The tape did not go to plan; every time played, I passed out. Andrea tried to increase the exposure hoping that eventually the impact would lessen. I could not even write down the time, Richard drove his Ferrari at 150mph at a brick wall, swinging the car at the last second so the rear end hit. He had threatened me that if he could not have me no one else would. I had clung to the seat belt, praying he would stop. He had asked me to go away with him and I had refused. It was later when I eventually met Joseph that he tried to kill me, by planning a motorway route and fixing the car so it would break down. The first nurse assigned to sit and listen to the tape, and support me, broke down, and had to excuse herself crying. She later came back and apologised.

The therapy had a huge risk involved with it, and irrationality and impulsivity became my dancing partners. I started to hoard more and more mugs and cutlery. I would pace the wards looking for anything to self-harm, and even with my level one nurse, would manage to store and hide items to use against myself.

One of my lowest points came when having a flashback and not being on level one, I raced past the nurses on duty and out into the hospital grounds. I headed down a slope to the shelter of a brick pillar.

Leaning against it to catch my breath I looked down, to my horror I was standing on a pile of used syringes and needles. Two male nurses came running over. They were not pleasant and one said, "Have you fucking shot yourself?" He scared me and I did not know what he meant.

"Okay," said the other one, "What the fuck have you taken?"

They marched, holding me in a special grip leading me to the ward. Karen came to meet them. "Think she's taken something, syringe on the ground," Karen shook her head as if to say no, and they went returning to their own wards. Upset I said, "I haven't, I haven't," and went to my room. I lay on the bed thinking, what am I doing here?

Later when I had calmed down, I rang Joseph, telling him I had changed my mind. How when I had tried to escape, two men were saying the 'F' word, and saying I had taken drugs. It was far from the truth. I was so against drugs. Joseph told me to hang on in there, and he put Jo Jo on to the phone. I changed my tone and spoke to her, teasing about school, she was laughing.

After I spoke to both children I had my tea early, I felt despondent and could see no way out. The men had been frightening, treating me like dirt. Changing into my nightshirt, I put on my silk dressing gown. Feeling bad, having nothing to lose I decided to try working at the past. I picked up a blank sheet of paper feeling so low, it did not matter which incident I wrote about. Did I write about my brother-in-law trying to kill me on the motorway, or other attempts on my life? Without thinking, I pulled off my silk dressing gown belt, tying it as tight as I could around my neck in a double knot. It was so tight I could not breathe properly. I sat propped up on my pillow facing the corridor at the stage of existing with no function. I became aware of Mark a staff nurse, he walked past the door looking across at me and continued. Next, he must have pulled his tag and I was vaguely aware of him shouting. My head by now felt as if it was exploding. I could feel my eyes coming out the sockets and the black was coming. Mark ran over to the bed, desperately tugging at the belt screaming for help, my head fell sideways as I was losing consciousness. I felt a nick on my neck and I passed out. I came to with a young woman Dr taking my pulse and telling them to monitor me through the night. They had nicked my neck but saved my life cutting the belt. Frankie a Chinese nurse who mostly worked nightshifts spoke, "Oh, Bridget, why?"

I could not speak; I did not really understand how it had happened. I had not planned it or meant it.

CHAPTER 5

High Secure Unit

I was standing in the High Street in Town. I had escaped and had obviously dissociated because I was not sure how I got there. I remembered panicking and bolting off the ward and running out of the car park. Now my mind was blank, luckily I had my mobile phone. I rang the ward and Barry answered. It was a relief as in times of distress ringing the ward was like Russian roulette. The wrong nurse with no empathy could send you spiralling down. Barry was a decent nurse and was immediately concerned, "Bridge, where are you, we have been looking for you, are you okay?"

"No," I could not speak, and held the phone to my ear hoping he would not stop talking. He was experienced enough to know I was having difficulty, and he continued to lead the conversation, "I guess you have ran for a while and ended up somewhere you didn't want to be, don't worry I can come and get you." I looked around; there was a pub opposite and a toyshop further up the road. I tried to speak. Barry carried on, "What ever you do, don't hang up, and if you do I'll ring you back, don't panic."

"High Street, Town," I muttered.

"Stay there, I am on my way."

I switched the phone off, and leant in the doorway. Opposite a commotion was going on and a huge crowd of youths came out of the pub yelling and shouting at each other. I moved further up the street, although I was across the road, I did not want trouble. Already, I could hear the sirens of a police van, and could just see the blue light at the top of the street. I crossed over to look in the toyshop for Jo Jo and Tee Jay. The siren was now deafening and as I looked, I was surprised, as the big white police van had drawn up next to me not the crowd. Before I could react, a police officer had jumped from the passenger seat and was approaching me warily. He halted a few feet away and I looked at him.

"Bridge?" he asked.

I nodded; he still kept his distance, "Are you okay?" Again, I nodded.

"Would you mind just sitting here with us; we will keep the door open?"

I followed him to the back of the van where his colleague sat. He waited expecting me to jump in, I did very slowly, and he continued to talk, "Barry rang us, he is on his way. Another van will take you back." As he was speaking, I could already hear another siren and to my surprise, another police van pulled up.

By this time, the crowd was watching me instead of me watching them. I felt embarrassed but calmly pulled a packet of mints from my pockets and offered them around. A taxi pulled up with Barry and he and I jumped into the front seats of the second van, after saying bye to the officers who had been very nice to me. They smiled and waved bye as they drove off. Barry and the new police officer joked all the way back to the hospital, and I felt relieved to be safe again.

The next weekend Joseph dropped a bombshell. It scared me more than I could ever let on. He had talked to Dr Lynn, who had given his permission, and had booked a holiday to Euro Disney. Jo Jo was excited and Joseph was ecstatic. I panicked, as the thought of travelling abroad and away from the hospital scared me. Joseph had not booked it just for us. He had booked it with our new neighbours, who I did not really know and we were to go together. It was expensive and I knew Joseph had made many sacrifices for this trip. I tried desperately to tell Ruth I was not ready for the trip. Ruth actually agreed as the trip was only weeks away. She promised to talk to Dr Lynn. My other neighbour and friend Joanie visited me, and she was convinced I was not ready for the trip. I had only moved to near Melton the previous year before going into hospital, and I barely knew the neighbours, they seemed lovely, but were still strangers. I had been in hospital for intensive therapy, some of which was life threatening. Unexpectedly, I was expected to be well enough to travel abroad with strangers, two young children under four and not only cope but be hundreds of miles away from the hospital.

I spent the next few nights sleeplessly, wondering how I would cope. I loved Joseph so much I could not tell him I was still struggling. Dr Lynn refused to listen, thinking the break would do me good. Only Ruth seemed to understand and all she could do was to shrug her shoulders. I became increasingly scared and one night hoarded many knives under my pillow. Lee was in a bad mood that evening, storming into my room and tipping the pillow off my bed. He grabbed the knives and mug pieces, shouting, "You think you're clever. You want to be on level one well you are not. Why don't you buck up and go home? You don't need to be here and you know it."

His words ate me up and returning to my room, and looking in the mirror, I hit myself hard on the cheek, then I punched myself on the other side. Alex happened to be on duty, and tried to get me to come out of my room. I was so upset I stormed up to Lee, "If I shouldn't be here then let me go home," I tried to walk past. He blocked the door.

"I don't need this, get back to your room," he scorned. I went back and then tried to go back down the corridor and out. Alex grabbed me, "Don't let him get to you, that's what he wants, don't do it Bridget."

I looked at her and could see the concern in her eyes. The next thing Lee shouted down the corridor, "It will be seclusion for you next, that will show you." I looked at him and in my hurt I hit myself, I couldn't hit him I used all my strength, and whacked my face and then I tried to bolt down the corridor to get out. Alex and another nurse threw themselves at me, pulling me down, "Please Bridget believe me, he's a bastard don't let him do it to you," Alex whispered in my ear.

They pulled me into my room and I fell on to my bed. I was determined Lee would not have the last say, and rang Joseph up. I told him Lee was threatening to put me in seclusion and had told me I should not be in hospital. Joseph asked if I was ok, he said, "You haven't done anything silly have you?" I hesitated, but knew he was going to see me at some time. "I bashed myself, look, he got me into such a state, he was saying to buck my ideas up, and I shouldn't be here and he was threatening seclusion. Dr Lynn would not have been happy."

"I am coming straight over; no don't tell him, I'll be there as quick as I can, let me ask Sophie to nip round for an hour." I shut the door and sat on my bed. Alex sat with me. "It's ok Joseph is coming down, he will sort him out."

It was an hour later when Joseph marched into my room. He had already seen Lee and was angry, "I asked him why you were in here. He said he didn't know, he hadn't even bothered to look at your file but you were a troublemaker." He then sat on the bed and looked at me, "Oh darling, what are they doing to you, don't let them get to you, they are supposed to help, not put you in this state," he gave me a hug and said, "He won't give you any more trouble. I have threatened to make an official complaint," I said goodbye to him and watched him walk down the corridor. I changed into my nightshirt and got into bed.

The next morning when I looked into my mirror, I could hardly see my eyes, my face had puffed up and my arm was sore. Later that morning when Dr Lynn walked in, he was visibly shocked. He stopped in his tracks and then continued to speak as if nothing had happened.

I continued to attempt to work at the past. It was difficult as little pieces entered my head, which I had completely forgotten about. They were unpleasant and I did not know how to handle them. If I was at home, I may have diverted by keeping especially busy, here it was hard to divert and was so boring I turned to the past more and more.

The time flew by and before I knew it, another incident happened. I had been hoarding all the mugs that I could get my hands on, placing them under the sink cupboard. I was having a drink of tea, whilst again working on my lifeline. This time I was trying to write a few more details in about my childhood. I suddenly knew I had to stop as my body started to shake and I felt extremely agitated. I turned to Stella a lovely nurse of mixed race and asked if we could go on a walk. She refused, as it was clear I was unwell. I could not accept her refusal, I was scared I would smash through the window, which I had done before and jump out. Stella said, "For God's sake, sit down and chill," she went to the door to call for some help and stepped out. In that second, I picked the chair up, and blocked her way in and picked up my mug. I moved quickly to the sink and when Stella shouted to me and made to come in, I threw a mug at the door. It smashed and she automatically jumped back. I picked another mug and was ready especially as she pulled the alarm, and nurses were running down the corridor to my room. Stella was furious and shouted some obscene language through the door. My response was to throw another mug, and every time someone tried to open the door, I threw one, making sure that I threw before the door could open wide enough.

My aim now was to keep safe and keep anyone out. I was scared and terrified they may put me in seclusion, or even drug me up. Luckily, the top ward manager was on and he sensibly told them to stop trying to come into my room and just observe and leave me alone. He sent the other nurses from other wards away. Time passed. I calmed down, and when I knew there was only Stella. I let her in. She quickly kept the door ajar, and another nurse came to sit the other side of me. Stella actually apologised and said she had been out of order. I felt embarrassed and apologetic and soon normal relationships continued.

Dr Lynn was firm the next day, telling me I should not put people's lives at risk. I thought he exaggerated as I only threw low and knew the door would not open. Yet I thought he would not know how rational or irrational I would have been.

As the holiday drew near, I panicked more and more, seizing any opportunity for self-harm. I now used the old ladies tights or stockings that would be hanging on the radiators to dry. I took the elastic cords off the bins. Any chance I could I would try to strangle myself. Caught twice, my level one was on high alert. I felt sorry for the old ladies and would go to the hospital shop with a nurse to replace their tights. They never knew the circumstances. I also tried to help as best I could, and would help the nurses with making the tea and biscuits.

The morning I was to go for the Disney break, I felt agitated and suicidal. Scared, I told Ruth and she again said she would speak to Dr Lynn. He brushed my feelings aside and said it was normal I would be anxious after such a long time in hospital, "Say hello to Mickey Mouse for me Bridge," he retorted as he left my room. He had signed me off level one, half-hour before I was due to go.

I felt odd and not at all safe, doing my best to keep any suicidal thoughts away. I was having thoughts of trying to run off the plane and of throwing myself off the hotel balcony. I did not know where to turn as everyone was wishing me well. I walked into the courtyard off the ward, and suddenly instead of returning to the ward, decided to try the door at the end.

Amazingly, it opened and I rushed through it quickly and ran to the nearest staircase. I ran up the stairs two at a time and came out on the top floor. I had made no plans and the first item that caught my eye was a fire extinguisher. I went to see if I could take it off the wall to smash through the top window and noticed that the security catch on the top part of the window had broken off the wooden frame. I looked at the other end and someone had broken both catches. I had shorts and trainers on, quickly jumping up on to the windowsill, I pulled myself up and climbed through the very top of the window. I felt free away from anyone, now precariously perched on the third floor up, and balancing on a 2" window ledge, with nothing to stop me falling except my hand clinging on to the frame. I looked around and noticed the cleaners starting to pull the curtains shut of windows below.

A nurse came out of the ward nearby took one look at me and ran back in. Soon there was a crowd of people on the ground and an even bigger crowd inside near the window. They could not reach up to me and were feeling too scared to come near and I stood there a bit lost. Tessa a nurse from my ward made her way through, "Hi Bridge, the dinner wasn't that bad was it?" she said laughing. "Worse, it was fish again," I replied back laughing. She laughed loudly. I laughed with her, but it was so false. Dr Lynn suddenly appeared looking very anxious and worried, "Bridge, what are you doing? Can you climb back inside and we can talk?"

I looked at the huge group of people behind him and knew immediately that if I came in, I would be taken to seclusion. I had heard about the seclusion rooms and it scared me. I shook my head. "Bridge, you don't want the fire engines here do you?" he asked. Again, I slowly shook my head. I could hear the sirens in the distance and when I looked down to the corridor in the distance, I saw two of my friends who looked like specs in the distance. They waved putting their hands to their mouths. I did not wave back. I was reluctant to move, as Dr Lynn was so tall he was one of very few people who could reach my hand if I put it on the edge. Yet if I did not, I would fall. The sun was beaming and the sweat poured off me. I moved my hand quickly. Dr Lynn moved with amazing speed and his hand grabbed my wrist. He was leaning through the narrow gap and had caught hold of my arm. Dr Lynn shouted to a young Chinese Dr to grab my shorts, and the poor chap climbed, leaning through and held on to my waistband. I was still using every inch of strength I had, to cling to the edge of the bricks. My foot kept slipping and although they held on to me, if my weight slipped I was not sure if I would fall from their grip to my death.

In the distance, I could hear the fire brigade. All I wanted was for people to disappear so I could get in and be on my own. I could now see over the lower rooftops and caught sight of the fire engine making its way over. It dawned on me I was in deep trouble. It was a no way back scenario, and I just clung on as the Junior Dr held my waistband, and Dr Lynn disappeared and reappeared on the ground talking to the firemen.

I was cursing my impulsivity, aware the sun was so hot. I was sweating and the fire brigade was putting up a ladder. They put another ladder up near by and a young fireman came up that one. An older man started to come up behind me. I stayed on the ledge, terrified and traumatised. I had firemen coming to the side, someone under and a load of people the other side of the glass.

Dr Lynn reappeared at the window, "Bridget they are going to talk you down, please do as they say." Knowing, there was no way I was going through the window, I stepped on to the ladder. I suddenly wanted to jump off and looked for a gap. Dr Lynn must have read my mind as he asked for the safety harness. The older fireman was now strapping this harness around me, as I was desperate to get away. I fiddled with the triangular catch. Yet the fireman was stronger and I could not undo it.

Eventually, I started to edge down the ladder with the encouragement of the elder one, as I drew level with the window, one of the nurses shouted "evil bastard," and I shot up the ladder again scared. It took the firemen another ten minutes to coach me down. The younger one was laughing asking me to hurry up, as they would all miss their tea break. They were nice, encouraging me all the time.

Thirty minutes later, I ended up on the roof of the next building. Still two storeys up, they had taken a window out to allow access for me from the roof to inside. The firemen escorted me over. A whole crowd of people stood in the room surrounding a chair. Dr Lynn was there beside the window. I freaked and bolted for the edge of the roof. I wasn't thinking, and would have gone straight over, if the fireman hadn't blocked me. Not allowed to touch me, they blocked the way. I looked for another exit and bolted in a different direction, again they beat me to it. I tried bolting under some thick pipes to the side. They stopped me again. It was as if we were playing rugby on the roof, and my touch was over the edge. My heart was racing, and I was determined to go over the edge to escape from the people inside. At no stage could I see that if I went over the edge I would not survive, all I could see was to escape from Dr Lynn and all the people in the room.

Suddenly, as I nearly managed to jump over, Dr Lynn shouted, "That's enough pick her up and carry her through." He was breaking the rules yet I nearly jumped to my death on the last attempt. The firemen picked me up as if I was a package and with great care and attention, they handed me over to the people waiting. I was pushed into the chair and told to sit for a few minutes, and then two of the male nurses grabbed my hands forcing me in the restraining lock, and we moved as a huge procession through the room, and out to the corridors.

Walking through a strange ward, on the way I stopped twice screaming with pain, as one of the male nurses was putting so much pressure on the restraining lock he was nearly breaking my wrist. I was not struggling, thinking he would release the tension. He increased it. Again, I stopped nearly collapsing, as the pain was awful.I was pushed into a small room. It had a tiny window with a wooden cross over it barring exit. To the side was a small toilet and shower, which was entered through a door. A mattress lay on the floor. Dr Lynn beckoned to Ruth and two other female nurses who were in there. He went out followed by the male nurses. He did not attempt to speak to me and I felt betrayed. Ruth spoke kindly to me, "Sorry, we are going to have to undress you. You have to wear one of these." The item she held up reminded me of a straight jacket. It was a tunic with no buttons or zips or anything that you could harm yourself with, having velcro fasteners.

The room was bare except for the mattress and a heavy cover. I followed instructions; the tunic stunk and was heavy. The room smelt of urine and little else. They shut the door. The room had three doors, each with a peephole, at different sides of the room so there was nowhere you could hide. I sat on the mattress and waited. There was nothing to do, and having spent many hours on renovating property, a damp patch on the wall drew my attention. I felt the paint and it peeled straight off. I did not get chance to think or do anything else, suddenly the door opened and Dr Lynn pushed in Joseph. I started to tell them about the damp patch. Dr Lynn turned quickly away and left.

Alone with Joseph we stared at each other, he looked visibly broken and I felt despair. We just walked to each other and hugged each other neither daring to let go. I did not want anything else except him and he wanted me. Neither of us had a chance to talk, a nurse appeared at the window. She came in shouting at Joseph saying he should not be with me. She tried to pull him off me; he turned and spoke harshly to her. The next thing, we were both surrounded by nurses, and Ruth was telling Joseph he should not be with me. We did not get the chance to say bye or even hug each other. Escorted out of the room struggling he looked back, mouthing 'love you,' I was upset and alone. I felt desperately sorry for him now his plans were in pieces. Not happy at the lack of privacy, I peeled some paint off the damp patch, covered each peephole, and sat on the mattress. I had no clue what was going to happen. I had been out in the sun for hours in the hottest time of day, and then stuck in a very hot room in a thick tunic with no drink offered. I went and lay down, a while later a different consultant came in, surrounded by nurses to talk to me. He asked me questions and at the time, I answered them angrily as I was not too happy to be stuck in a small room, with no one letting me know what was happening.

A social worker visited me later informing me, I was to be moved to the high secure unit across Leicester as soon as a bed became free. I still had no offer of food or drink.

My next visit was the night staff at about 9.30pm, asking if I wanted a drink of water. I was so grateful I sipped at the plastic cup aware that the more I drank, the more I would need the toilet. The next morning after spending a miserable night under flickering lights, I was told, Joseph had still taken the children to Euro Disney with the neighbours.

I was glad that the children had the chance to go. Although I was sad, as it was a dream to go to Disneyland, I was relieved, as I knew I was not well enough to have gone at the time.

An ambulance came for me at about half past ten. Supervised, I dressed back into my clothes. I had an escort of two nurses, a male, and female. Karen the nice West Indian nurse was the female, plus the ambulance staff to the high secure unit. They told me, my belongings would be in the ambulance in a black bin bag.

Arriving at the secure unit, a nurse stood either side holding on to each of my arms, and one of the staff carried my bag. We had to be let into a secure porch, and then again let in through secure doors to the unit. Walking through, I was not allowed any of my personal things, having to give my wash bag in. I had to ask for a hairbrush or toothbrush, and give it back after. A drinks machine operated by tokens stood in a corner. Eating time, we were escorted to a small canteen.

The unit only held ten patients, there was only one other female. My room was like a prison cell, with a huge metal door with peepholes, a tiny wardrobe, and a small toilet. A small man with greasy hair introduced himself. He offered no hand, telling me his name was Joe. He spoke gruffly, "You are not allowed bed sheets here, unless you earn them."

I purposely showed no emotion and merely nodded. He led me to my bedroom instructing me to hang my clothes up. I immediately had a problem; one bag was mine the other was not. I had no underwear and limited clothes. Joe had left the room, when this tall lanky lad with a glazed look scared me, as he blocked the door and then turned and started to go through the little clothes I had. At the first opportunity, I bolted, beating him to the door and ran to the nearest staff for help. I was shaken up, as within an hour of arriving a complete stranger who was well out of it had trapped me on my bed.

The staff apologised, telling me he had just moved out of the room and had obviously mistaken it for his and he was unwell. They led him away. I went and sat on a nearby bench. Most of the nurses were in a staffroom that looked like a greenhouse made of mostly glass. They could see most of the sitting area and the leisure room having a snooker table. Alongside was a tiny room with books and music and a play station. The only other female occupant called Sheila was a dark younger woman, with an afro haircut and big brown eyes. She was nice to me asking me why I was there. She came to my rescue about the underwear, having a brand new sealed set of pants a size bigger. I was so grateful. She and Joe sat either side of me and gave me a few tips of keeping away from the other inmates.

Joe was criticising me for smashing all the windows at the other hospital, and as much as I tried to explain, I had not purposely done it, he did not seem to believe me. I also made it clear I had offered to pay for damages yet he did not seem to believe that. I eventually gave in, as I had gauged the best way to keep the peace or get on, was to let him believe you needed his advice and support.

I went and sat in a nearby lounge and another occupant who looked like he could have been Asian, came, and sat next to me. He whispered in my ear, "If I killed you tonight no one would know, they would just think you were asleep." I looked at him, he was laughing. I was not sure how much he was joking or warning me off, I was determined to show he had not scared me and stayed sitting next to him. At the same time, I was making a note; I would not sit next to him later.

One of the other occupants scared me; he was a lot older and had long straggly greasy hair. His face wizened, he smoked non-stop. He would sit and suddenly start shouting. It was unnerving and I tried to stay in a different room.

A young lad, blonde and around 18 years old, asked me to play snooker, I enjoyed playing. He won but it was not a whitewash, and later when the staff changed, one of the male nurses gave me some tuition.

I went to bed that night on a mattress and a single cover. I kept my clothes on, not sure how clean the mattress was. I decided no matter what, I would keep to my morals and aim to be pleasant, helpful and to get on and hopefully out.

I missed having my phone. The pay phone in the hallway was not very private. As Joseph was away, I asked Paula who was a Home Start volunteer and good friend, to visit; Mum came to see me too. Both were upset, shocked at having to pass their handbag over to be searched, and at the conditions of the unit.

Although I had never been in a jail, it reminded me of one. The metal doors slammed shut and the sound of the keys locking some of the doors echoed down the corridor. One of the better things about the place besides the snooker table and play station was the food. It was fantastic and I could not believe the iced cream cakes for pudding.

One of the other occupants also unnerved me; he was similar looking to the lanky person who had taken over my room. He was mid twenties and unshaven and was smoking a used cigarette stub. He offered me a draw and I smiled refusing politely. "Do you know something?" he leant over to me, and I grimaced inhaling his smoky breathe. "Someone's going to die here tonight." Again, I was not sure how to respond to this, so desperately tried to acknowledge it, without showing any sign of emotion.

In the evening as I sat on the settee, I was horrified when the Asian lad who had threatened to kill me jokingly or not, came and sat beside me. I was just wondering how to deal with the situation, when his parents arrived. Sitting next to him, they brought out a big greasy looking paper bag with something hot inside. The woman who I presumed to be his Mum, dressed in a striking sari leant over and offered me the bag. She was gesturing and nodding, and to be polite I took a hot samosa out of the bag. I bit in to it, as she was waiting for a response. It was hot and very spicy, nearly making me cough. I swallowed hoping my eyes would not water and smiling I raised my thumb. She was delighted and said something to me that I did not understand. Later after they had gone, their son stood up and beckoned me to follow him, I did cautiously and sighed a breath of relief as he passed me a snooker cue and started to set the balls up.

In the evening, one of the male nurses called Andy came to talk to me again. He warned me to be always careful when I played snooker, "These guys are really sick," he said, "And one of these balls could be lethal."

I still tried to do my best, and the second night one of the nurses had smiled and had helped me make my bed. She too had apologised, and said I should have had the sheets from the beginning. I said nothing, as I did not want to get Joe into trouble. I got on really well with Sheila, and we became friends, she too liked to write and she showed me some articles she had done. I was impressed and encouraged her.

She was not allowed to go to the pottery session, so I went without her. I made a small basket. I felt it was very patronizing treating us like toddlers. Yet it killed some time. One of the younger looking lads with blonde hair attached himself to me, sitting next to me wherever I sat. I liked him, and he told me he had come from the ward above me at the other hospital. Another person also came from that ward, he was called Simon and was due to go back the next day. He promised to visit me when he returned.

Altogether, I stayed there five days, and although there were some horrific frightening periods, when some of the inmates acted out, and I would shake from head to foot, I enjoyed the snooker and meeting Sheila.

On the journey back, I was shocked to hear I was being transferred upstairs. I panicked in the taxi, asking to go back to the secure unit. I had heard so much about upstairs, and seen the state of some of the people. Some were from the city, dressed, and acting way out. Some so drugged up they scared me.

I was still upset, arriving at hospital, and would have jumped from the taxi except the doors had been locked. I refused to go upstairs and sat in the reception. I was thinking of my room, I had called it my room. I was devastated to be moving, most of the staff had become like a huge family to me. A few had been nasty but they were in the minority, and I was terrified of going upstairs.

Eventually two nurses came down to greet me from the new ward. One had long dark hair and a nice face; the other had a cheeky grin and blonde hair. I tried desperately to get out of going, I pleaded with the nurses from the secure unit to take me back. They both kissed me and told me they had to go. The first ward was now only for the elderly, mother and baby, for Dr Lynn and the rest of his patients had gone upstairs. I had no choice, the cheeky nurse, was also called Bridget, and she persuaded me with Melanie, the dark haired one, to go upstairs with them. I immediately thought if we went up the stairway, I could bolt for the first window and escape. I agreed to go with them.

Standing up, each of them took one of my arms, holding me in the restraining grip, held to go to the seclusion room. This time neither held me tight, nor hurt. I walked with them through the doors and headed for the stairway, they pulled me back. "No Bridget, we take the lift."

I breathed deeply and sighed, and they both laughed. It was at that moment I knew, they knew what I had been thinking and I grinned in defeat as we headed for the lift.

Showing me into my own room, the ward was similar to downstairs, my belongings were in my room, and there were loads of bags. Melanie and Bridget handed me over to an older nurse, who smiled and introduced herself as Beryl. She was amazed at how much belongings I even had tennis racquets and my portable television. My main priority was to put up Jo Jo's pictures everywhere.

It was an hour later when I went into the kitchen for a cup of tea. I bolted straight out, as a stranger walked through and Beryl asked another nurse to make us a drink. I realised I was back on close level ones, as the nurse who replaced Beryl was in close proximity at all times. I had to have the door ajar when I went to the toilet. I was so used to this, resigning myself to the fact that it would be worse for the person watching.

I soon learnt that level ones had to be taken with a pinch of salt, as consistency never happened. The nurses changed every hour, one hour someone could be so closely watching me, they could have told me how many times I blinked, and another hour I could walk out the room and tell the person who was watching me that I was going. My feelings on this inconsistency were ambivalent, when I was feeling fine, I was glad when I was not watched closely, as when they did, it made me want to scream. However when I was ill and panicking, I was scared, as I knew, if I tried to kill myself on impulse, a nurse who was not conscientious, could cost me my life. I was therefore grateful and respected the nurses who took their job seriously.

I also understood it was difficult for some of the nurses to comprehend how serious the situation was, as 70% of the time I was probably saner than some of the staff. I also behaved impeccably, so the majority of the time was a model patient. Having respect for others, I also offered to go to the shop when the nurses wanted, fetch dinners, do routine jobs etc, so some of the time, it was easy for some of the nurses to become complacent.

I used this complacency to my advantage, and would stock up to the hilt with things that were detrimental to my well being, such as extra cutlery, more mugs, hiding knives under the sheets, breaking knives in two etc. I would pump for information and would find out who was on duty, and would try to make this to my advantage, as some nurses were so professional I wanted to use their expertise, and when the poorer ones were on, would concentrate on other issues.

The surrounding environment had a knock on effect to my health. Some days, when I was having flashbacks and was not stable, if the nurses on duty were not helpful, or showed no empathy, it could fuel my instability, and I would act out, becoming impulsive and dangerous to myself. This would be a vicious circle. If the nurses were not able to manage it correctly, I would not either.

Another patient on the ward, a woman in her fifties called Alison, walked round with both hands in her front jean pockets, swaggering about in trainers and sweatshirt. Anyone she took a dislike to, she told to fuck off.

One nurse told me that she had burnt a hostel down. I attempted to keep out her way, yet, as I was on level one, Alison took it into her head, that I was someone who was massive trouble, who would be good to get to know. She started to chat to me and I responded, mainly out of curiosity.

Soon we were having coffee together, and she would come and visit me in my room. Her key worker was a nurse who detested me, and had it in for me all the time. The next day walking around the hospital grounds with my level one nurse, Alison walked up and tagged along. Bending down to do my laces up near some broken glass, I picked up some pieces putting them into my pocket, my trusting nurse had not seen. I was not going to use it, just store it. Alison saw me do this and thought it was hilarious. She laughed all the way back, and I wished she had not been with me.

Once back in my room, I hung my coat up, full of the glass. I then went to make another drink, and made one for the nurse who was with me. The next day, things kicked off, Alison was in a foul mood and warned a few times, as she became very violent, swearing, kicking doors, and knocking tables over. She did not come to see me and I was not bothered, as I thought it better to keep my distance.

Andrea came that afternoon. We were discussing some writing and drawings I had done, when there was a knock at the door. It was Alison's key nurse, throwing me a scornful look, she said, "Can I have a word?"

Andrea followed her to the door. There was some whispering and Andrea came back refusing to let her in, saying she would deal with it. "Have you got some glass in your room?" She looked directly at me, nodding I went and took it out of my pocket and gave it to her.

"Did you give a big piece to Alison?" Andrea asked. I shook my head, "No, I'd never do that, you know that."

Andrea nodded, "Yes, I do believe you." She went to the door and asked a nurse to take over whilst she got rid of the glass.

I was fuming, I told Andrea that Alison was trying to set me up, and her key nurse would be the first to take advantage. Andrea had to be professional, "I believe you, that's what matters." When leaving, she put her hand reassuringly on my shoulder, "Take care, and let it go," she walked out of my room. Melanie came and sat with me, she was my key worker and one of the nurses in charge. "Let it go, Bridget, you and Alison come from completely different backgrounds, don't get involved."

My pride would not let it go, and I went out of my room looking for Alison, she was just coming out of the smoke room. She looked up at me scowling, walking away into the kitchen. I was not having it. I followed her. She had her back to me, making a drink and I looked around making sure there was nothing dangerous she could use to attack me. "Why?" I asked.

It was enough to set her off. She turned quickly eye balling me, "Fuck you, fuck everyone," taking a step towards me, I held my ground; she stormed out slamming the door. I was shaking, but pleased I had stood up to her, no one was going to dominate me. I walked back to my room and sat on the bed. "Alright?" asked Melanie. She had witnessed all of it.

"Fine, I needed to clear it up," I smiled, asking if she wanted anything at the shop. We stayed working together on my writing and pictures.

Some of the lads on the ward were characters. I was scared of a few rough looking ones. Yet one of the tough guys kept coming up to me for a chat. He even offered to make me a drink. His name was Billy; he was about 5 ft 8, unshaven, had one earring and half his head was shaven, the other not. On his arm, he had tattoo of a serpent, looking like it moved, when he bent his arm. When he called by my room, I shouted and offered him a biscuit. He and a few lads were fine. I kept clear of some who I knew would become violent unexpectedly.

I had to take a lot of stick, having a permanent companion, and some of the patients were actually jealous. They shouted and made fun of me in a nasty way. It hurt at the beginning, but I became used to it and ignored them.

I was sitting on my bed waiting for Dr Lynn. I knew he was coming as I had just passed the nurses station. He had kept to his word and seen me nearly every day. Next to me was my work, and I had once again, drawn many pictures, drawing helped me concentrate on the detail, this actually diverted me from the real reason I was drawing it. Dr Lynn entered the room and sat in the comfortable green leather chair. I was comparing the patterns of the rope I had drawn, to the ones on his tie. He did his usual staring trick, just sitting, not saying anything. This always made me uncomfortable, although I knew it was part of the therapy. Freethinking to see what came into my mind, sometimes I would sit there, and not talk for ages, either. Today he broke the silence. "I know you could not manage the tape about your brother-in-law, don't worry I am not going to ask you to do that, but I want to go over how you found your real Dad?" I looked at him in dismay,

"I didn't find him, she did, and you know that. This was before I had my own house and worked for my brother-in-law, it's history, not important."

He leant back in his chair crossing his long legs and said, "Go on then, if it's not that important." Hesitating, I fiddled with my pen and sat staring at my bed. "I am not forcing you Bridge, but try to start at the easiest place," Dr Lynn spoke very quietly and calmly. I began thinking of how I got involved with the vet.

CHAPTER 6

The Vet

Jena my dog was having real ear problems. The next time I went to the vet, he suggested some different ear treatment as her ear was not improving and the discharge was terrible. I agreed, hesitating, and he asked me why. I explained that due to ME, I had finished work and although I was hoping to be working full time soon, I was having some financial difficulties. As I spoke, I blushed, feeling embarrassed. The vet was not too bothered and was chatty. He asked what I was doing now, knowing I had previously been working in a shop.

Watching him disinfect the stainless steel table, I explained, I had just started to work a few hours doing engineering, I joked about how I had done plastering in the house, plasterboard partitions, wiring, and now I was doing part time engineering.

As I looked up, he grinned and said, "Joke no more, I have the perfect solution," he stopped wiping the surface and continued, "I've another property I'm working on at weekends, and I could do with some help, if you come the odd Saturday and Sunday and help me, I'll help you with free treatment for the dog."

I stood back, I had not expected this sort of suggestion, but all of a sudden, the cloud above me started to lift, as the pressure of each week, not knowing where to find the money for Jena was disappearing.

"The first job is to fit kitchen units, and I expect you to use the drill," he was

looking at me waiting for a reply. I hesitated, "I can use a drill and I'll put the units up, but I have to work depending on how fit I am."

He crossed the room and shook my hand, "Fine, I'll pick you up at 2.30pm on Saturday." I was ushered out of the room and grabbing Jena's lead I left. I half skipped going home. I was feeling as if weights from my shoulders were slipping off. The worry of paying for Jena had eaten at me enormously, and the fact that I still had a debt of £2000 around my neck.

Unlatching the gate I walked up our massive driveway, I felt there was a god after all. I was tired as I walked through the back door, but Mum knew straight away that something had happened. "How did you get on?" she asked, continuing to peel the potatoes. I walked over and thrust the kettle under her nose, as I started to fill it. "He wants me to help him, he's doing up a house and needs weekend help, as it will pay for Jena's treatment, I said yes." I turned and started to put two mugs out, and put a teabag in one and a spoon full of coffee in the other. Mum hardly drank tea, always preferring coffee, unless there were a few of us, and then she would do a big teapot. She turned, and as she placed the potatoes on the hob said, "You be careful, don't you go over doing it." I looked at her with her apron on, and never stopping, but kept quiet.

"He knows I've been ill, Mum and it will help with the cost for Jena, and the cats' boosters when they're due." The kettle was boiling and as I poured, Mum sat down and said, "When are you starting?" sipping her coffee, before I could answer, she continued. "What about Richard and the work for him, will he mind, does he want you at the weekends?"

I sipped my tea and got up to let Jena in, who was scratching at the door. "Mum, Richard hasn't discussed work and I'm not tied to him. If he asks me for weekend work, I'll probably help him but he hasn't, and I have to pay for Jena, I don't know how many weekends he wants me, I'll take things as they come. I will also have to let Sandra know as she still expects me there." Mum said nothing, and I knew she wouldn't mind me not going to Sandra's, as she felt hurt that I often picked Sandra over her. I could not explain to Mum how deep my feelings were for Sandra. I did not understand it myself. All I knew was that when I was younger and alone, it was Sandra who had gone out of her way to make me feel special and shown an interest in my homework, and Sandra with Mum's encouragement had persuaded me to get out of the house, and had introduced me to her family.

Somehow, with Sandra I had felt as if I belonged. At home, I loved Denny but she was a real extrovert, always with lots of friends. I loved Jane.Yet she and I were miles apart. Our tastes, principles, and attitudes were very different. Mum was always busy, and Dad if he was not at the club, was at either the masons or gardening. Susanne was my best friend, but she helped her Mum a lot of the time.

On Saturday, I was nervous as I felt like it was the start of a new job and employer.The vet called at 2.30pm, I grabbed my denim jacket pushing Jena into the car alongside the tools and alarm. Mum waved me off at the door.

The house was a semi-detached cottage a few miles away, sweet with a stable door to the back and a tiny yard.The back door led into the kitchen.There was a sink but nothing else; the units were in parts on the floor. Mark the vet said, "Come and look at the rest of the house," he walked across the hall and through to another room. Looking up, I could see another two floors up, as most of the roofs and floorboards were missing. I followed Mark up a winding staircase to the next floor level.

The air was full of plaster dust, part of the room half partitioned with plasterboards, and for some unknown reason, a corner newly plastered. "Hopefully with you on board, we can get this room done too," Mark smiling looked down at me. I followed him further up the stairway.

Here it was peculiar, the entrance bricked over, and to the side, a hole dug into the wall. I walked through, amazed at the sight.We were in a sort of bedroom, there was a carpet with a double bed, and a television on the wall, adjoining a little kitchen place, with a sink and kettle, and some mugs. Mark said, "Here's where we can have a coffee break, I am not a slave driver all the time."We both laughed together, and then he led me downstairs back to the original kitchen, and literally placed a drill into my hand. I looked closer at the units, which were made of a real nice pine; frameworks already on the wall and one unit started. "Where are the screws?" I asked. Mark pointed to a small cloth bag, "All the sizes are in there, drill bits and other tools in that box, and the unit with the patterned shelf is the third one along." I nodded, picking up the tape measure to double check where I thought I was supposed to drill.

I had just started to drill, when the door opened, and Mark's wife came in. She was very glamorous and smiled at me. She had some plaster nails and the special raw plugs that go into plaster. Mark introduced her to me, "This is Shirley," we shook hands and I smiled, she smiled back and commented, that she had seen me plenty of times when I had visited the surgery. I knew this as she was often in the receptionists' room chatting to the girls. I had also seen her with her greyhounds.

"We must get together sometime;" she said, "To take the dogs out together." I nodded in agreement, continuing to put up the units. She did not stay long and the afternoon shot by. Mark insisted we went upstairs for a drink, and I cautiously drank a mug of tea, not sure, if a toilet was working. I enjoyed that afternoon.

Mark picked me up at 11.30am on the Sunday. He always had his mobile phone with him, in case someone needed to bring an animal in for an emergency. I was shocked at how he answered to some patients, telling one person to fuck off, saying did not they understand that vets had to have some time off. He was not rude to me and even complimented me on my work. I managed to finish the units on the Sunday and looked forward to doing the plasterboards.

Mum and Dad went away on the Tuesday, and I enjoyed having the place to myself. On Wednesday evening, the doorbell went at around 7.30pm, I undid the front door, surprised to see Mark standing there, relieved, as it was someone I knew. It was raining, and I opened the door, asking him if he wanted to come in. He did, following me through to the lounge, "I'm not disturbing you am I?" he asked taking his cap off and smoothing his hair back. "No, not at all, do you want a drink?" I asked.

"Great, tea with 2 sugars, thanks," he replied. Mark followed me into the kitchen, "Shirley asks if you will go for a walk with her on Friday, with the dogs at 9.30. She will pick you up, and also can we start at 1.30pm on Saturday instead of 2.30pm, as we are out later and I want to finish earlier?" He stood behind me, watching as I made his tea. I could smell tobacco on his jumper, and I answered passing him his drink, "Yes to both, will Jena be ok with your dogs?"

He nodded, following me to the lounge, where I gestured him to sit down, sitting back on my cushion I sat up leaning against the settee.

Mark sat on the settee just behind me, and stretched his legs, he then carried on talking, telling me about his day at the surgery. He also told me how nice it would be for Shirley to see me, as she did not know many people. "How come you're living here, not with your partner?" he asked

"Partner? I don't have a partner," I looked at him puzzled, laughing he continued, "Well you always came to the surgery together and according to my records, you lived together and had the same pups from the same litter, the whole village see you work together also." I felt myself going red and hot, and knew I was blushing. I was just going to answer when he continued, "I just assumed you were an item."

"Well you can unassume, because we certainly aren't. I am living back with Mum and Dad because of my illness, Sandra is still a friend of mine, but she has a friend called John and that's all we are," I was not sure if I was cross or upset or both.

Dr Lynn asked, "Was that the first time someone had asked, if you and Sandra were together?" I looked at him, not answering, and continuing

.

"Sorry, I obviously have it wrong," Mark leant forward, placing his hand, on my shoulder, to pacify me. Yet I was not calm, I continued to say how Sandra had helped me when I was younger. How she had helped me find my Mum, and before I knew it, I was telling him, how much I had struggled. I was so intent on making sure he did not think we were an item. I loved Sandra like another Mum or sister.

I drank the rest of my drink, suddenly realizing that I was leaning against him, and that he had moved from the settee to the floor, and was being supportive. I was embarrassed, too scared to move, and sat there in silence. He apologized jumping to his feet. I led the way out, Mark said, "Don't worry, we'll look after you, see you on Saturday at 1.30pm, don't forget to see Shirley on Friday, ring her if you can't make it." He then gave me a quick kiss on the cheek and walked quickly down the driveway. I closed the doors, locked up, and went back inside, feeling as if I had dreamt the last hour. I put the kettle back on and switched the television over to watch the news.

On Friday morning I wore boots as it was raining, and a waterproof coat, I was not sure if Shirley would turn up. At 9.30, she arrived, laughing at me squeezing Jena on to the back seat with her two dogs. We drove in through the north end of the park, and walked pleasantly through to the largest lake. Shirley questioned me a lot, and asked me some personal things about my life. I gathered from the conversation, Mark had said some things to her, and I felt committed to explaining more when she asked. Shirley asked, why I didn't want to find my real Dad, and I said I had never given the matter a lot of thought, as I had always concentrated on finding my Mum. According to the counsellor and information given, he was not interested in my Mum or the baby. Shirley listened and asked if I had his name, I had and as I told her, I splashed through the next puddle in frustration. Shirley asked, "Why don't you look through the Plymouth directory and send a letter if the name exists?"

I hesitated, "What about my Mum's or Dad's reaction if a letter came through our doorway?"

"Use the address at our other house, I'll check for responses," said Shirley, "I'll write the letter." I felt a bit taken back but she was trying to be so helpful that I agreed.

In the next few weeks, I saw quite a bit of Shirley, and she drafted a letter to my real Dad. She stated that I was desperate to meet and that if it were he, would he reply. I signed the letter, we sent it to the one name that matched my real Dad's details, and the address was in Plymouth.

The following weekend I was at the house with Mark working on the floorboards. It was a dangerous job as there were huge gaps and with no floors, a big drop. We walked across the joists balancing, starting to put the floorboards down from the far end. I was nervous, yet enjoying the challenge, and the danger of the situation raising my adrenalin levels, gave me a constant buzz. Shirley called in a couple of times bringing some spare nails. She liked to monitor our progress. Then she would disappear back to shopping or taking her dogs for a walk.

Upstairs, we worked hard and had a great system where Mark would fit the floorboard, and I would fix it down with hammer and nails. The pace was so fast, a mistake sent the routine out. I hit my thumb, yet did not dare stop. The floorboards were well over half way done, when I decided I needed to go to the toilet. I had been *hanging on, but was now on my limit. I was embarrassed, not even sure, if there was a working loo there. I looked up, "Where's the loo? Sorry I need to go."*

To my surprise, Mark laughed, and got up too, "It's on the floor below us, here I'll show you," without waiting for me to get up, he sauntered off down the staircase. I rushed to catch up, following him, across an empty room to the doorway, where he pointed. It was so urgent; I pushed the door open realising there was no lock, and that the door did not even shut properly. I hesitated, having no choice. The loo was filthy, and I crouched over it in an undignified manner, conscious that Mark had not left the room, embarrassed that he was just the other side of the door. Finished, I was yanking my jeans up, when the door opened. Mark grabbed my arm pulling me out, we both crashed to the ground. I had no chance to react as he was on top of me pulling my underwear down. I struggled. He was too strong, mouth hard on mine. He was in an excited state, moving himself up and down on my body. His hands were between my legs, forcing them apart. His jeans zip tearing into my flesh. Then he entered me, and as the pain erupted, I saw the safe, files, and saw a picture of blood on the floor. I dissociated, the black swamped me, and for a while, I was spaced out and in a safe place. This place was mine, nobody could reach me there, and it was peaceful...

"Bridget, Bridge are you ok? Someone get her a drink of water." I came round and found myself sitting on the hospital floor leaning against my bed. Dr Lynn was leaning anxiously over me taking my pulse. I struggled to recall what had happened. "Why are you here? What am I doing?" I said. "Don't you remember?" he asked frowning. I shrugged. I was not sure what had happened, "I can remember you coming into the room." I squinted, trying hard to remember. "Don't worry, rest and you can continue tomorrow," Dr Lynn spoke, beckoning a nurse to stay, he left the room.

Two days later, he asked if I could remember where we had reached. I tried my hardest to continue.

I came to lying on the bed in the small bedroom. Mark was sitting next to me with a mug of tea. He seemed very concerned, "Are you feeling better?" He was so caring and nice. I was completely confused, feeling woozy headed, and I just nodded, sipping the tea. Mark drank his, and disappeared. Not wanting to stay in the bedroom, I went through to where he was working. I picked up the hammer to finish the job.When we finished, Mark turned, grinning, "Well we have done well today, haven't we?" I nodded, pleased that the room was finished, and looking forward to doing the plasterboards. Mark fumbled into his coat pocket bringing out two yellow looking tubes. "Jena, might respond better to these."

He dropped me off at the gate, telling me he would pick me up at 2pm the next day. I slowly walked up the drive to Mum's and Dad's clutching Jena's medication in my pocket, and focused on the plasterboard.

The next day dawned and I ignored the bruising on my leg where the zip had caught me. I was looking forward to putting the plasterboards up. The harder I worked, the more satisfaction I got, yet I knew I had to pace myself. Sunday afternoon was nice weather wise, and at 2pm, I was waiting at the bottom of the drive. Mark pulled up, and Jena jumped in and went straight onto the back seat, she was a great dog and very abiding.

We arrived at the house and I headed straight upstairs to the room, and then realising, went charging back downstairs, as we had to carry the plasterboards all the way up. I was amazed at Marks strength, I could carry one board at a time all the way upstairs, and he would take three.

At 4pm, Mark called me through the hole in the wall for a large steaming mug of tea. I stared around the carpeted little room that seemed strange when the rest of the house was in bits with floorboards out. Mark had already started on the bathroom, and there were gold plated taps shining like a beacon from a lighthouse. Finishing my tea, I quickly went through the mouse hole. Mark grabbed me from behind. I fell, landing backwards heavily. Mark pulled me towards him, creating carpet burns up my body. Madly pulling my shoes and jeans off, rubbing his hands up and down my thighs, his eyes had a glazed look. He started to make circular movements, rubbing on different areas of my body, naming different animals and sexual activities. He sat up laughing, "A dog's sexuality would be around here,"he muttered. He seemed to take great delight in doing everything in slow motion, and every second my adrenalin was pumping harder and harder.Yet

I had no reactions. He suddenly changed, as if possessed; pulling my head back, I thought my neck was going to break then I was in the dark.

I woke up, lying on the bed, and could not keep my eyes open. Mark was taking my pulse, I struggled trying to work out what was happening. I swung my feet and got up, swaying I grabbed the bed. Mark went through the mouse hole and I followed gingerly. He looked at me for a comment and I replied, "We have done a good job, do you have the wood for the skirting boards ready?" He pointed to the other doorway, and I could see a pile of timber already cut at the corners. "I don't mess around you know," he said, and I smiled back at him.

Dr Lynn leaned forward in his chair. "How can you smile at someone who has just viciously raped you?" There was a long silence as I tried to justify my actions. "I don't know. I was concentrating on the work and was pleased that we had that room sorted." He did not reply, shaking his head and putting his hand to his forehead, "Ok Bridget, we'll continue tomorrow." He left the room and I asked the nurse if we could go and get a drink.

The next day he seemed irritated, as I continued to tell him some of my past.

The next weekend was sunny, and Shirley came with us. We started on the next room. A few floorboards lay in place on the edge, but the rest of the floor needed finishing. Shirley had gone on through the mouse hole into the makeshift kitchen and I went downstairs and started to bring up the timber for the floorboards. It was awkward as the timber was long, the staircase was narrow and bent, and they would only go up at the right angle. I struggled attempting to do my best.

Shirley asked, if I would go out with her in the week with the dogs and I told her I would love to. She turned, as she put on her coat saying, "I'll leave you two to it then and don't be late tonight, remember we are out." We started the same routine as before, Mark laying the wood down, and I hammering it on the joists having most of the floor down before lunch. We stopped at one o'clock to tuck into a couple of cobs each, I was hungry and thirsty, but I tried to limit my drinking not wanting to go to the loo again.

After, as I sat nailing the wood onto the joist, I looked down, through two floor levels to the ground floor. A pile of letters caught my eye, and I wondered if my Dad had written back. I was leaning over to pick the hammer up, when Mark caught hold of my hand, and pulled it, sending me completely off balance forward onto my front, my face ending up on his leg. "Got you now," he laughed, pulling me on top of him and I grabbed at him, because I was on the edge of the floorboards. He held my jeans stopping me from crashing through the floors to the ground. He moved me to the edge, frantically pulling my jeans down, and I tried holding on to his leg with one hand, the other held the edge of the boards. Ripping his clothes off, he kept pushing me gently onto the edge, at the same time clutching my wrist, rolling on top of me, breathing heavily into my neck, his eyes focusing on the drop below us, exciting him repeatedly.

This world was in my dreams. Only I lived in it, and it was up to me how I handled it. If I kept busy, it would go away, and not be there. Only I was aware of it, no one else, and one day it would go, to tell someone would make it alive and real. I did not want that. I wanted it to stay a bad dream where the dark took over and then when you awoke it had gone.

Now he was crazy, the way he kept looking over the edge, seemed to send him on a real high. He thrust himself inside me and raised himself up and down at an alarming rate. His eyes were glazing over, although I could not move, it was roles reversed. He was not here, he was miles away, thrusting hard, through my body and I felt this time I was going to die…

Eventually he finished and walked away. I wanted to move but I was still unable to react, and could only lie there, keeping my weight away from the edge. I dare not close my eyes in case the black came, and I went over. He went out through the door. I could hear him going downstairs. I couldn't turn to see if he was underneath watching, I felt his presence was there, but I waited until my feelings came back, and when they did I rolled away from the edge, put on my clothes and continued to hammer the nails in.

Mark returned with some drinks passing me a mug. I put it down, near to where I was working and continued, no words passed, until all of a sudden he said, "Crikey, it's gone past five, we'd better rush."

He dropped me off at the gate and I went inside calling Jena, pocketing the new yellow tubes, he had given to me. Jena's ears did not seem to be improving a lot, but they were not getting worse.

Shirley and I received a reply back from Plymouth. It turned out to be my biological Dad and he had asked to see me. Shirley repeatedly insisted I needed some counselling or help. She told me I ought to go and visit my real Dad. I was very mixed as I did not want to upset my Mum and Dad, yet needed in my own heart to go down and meet him.

Friday dawned and I was getting ready to go to work, the post came and Mum handed me a hand written letter. I went to sit on my own bed to read it. It was an unpleasant letter telling me, I was not needed at the house, and banned from the surgery. It was so unexpected, that I was upset, and Mum came in to see why I had not appeared at the table. I showed her the letter and she was as shocked as I was, and just said wait until she saw either of them. She went to tell Dad. He was also upset, especially as recently he had taken time off to help me deliver a load of plasterboards to the house, and I had shown him all the work we had done. It was not long after that letter that I saw Shirley in the local shops, and she waved and said, "Hello," as if nothing had happened.

I had been telling Dr Lynn my recollection as if I was talking about the weather. I had no emotion and was matter of fact about it all. He asked Andrea to discuss some of it with me and again, I felt nothing.

Jo Jo and Tee Jay came in at weekends, and I missed my family dreadfully. I missed Joseph, yet I could not handle visitors very well. My friends Tom and Susanne came to see me, and they commented that I should be at home with my family. It made me feel guilty and again I questioned whether I should be in the hospital. It made me feel my past was not significant, and I should either have dealt with it or moved on, or I was making too big a deal out of it.

Dr Lynn decided to ask me about my real biological Dad, and he asked Andrea to discuss how I met my Dad. I again tried to relate back to how I came to meet him and describe as best I could to Andrea.

CHAPTER 7

My Biological Dad

I had been with Richard a few weeks and because Shirley had put the idea in my head of meeting my Dad, I decided to go and meet him. Sandra did not want me to go on my own, so we decided to go down south for a weekend. A good enough excuse to say I was going away for a few days to Mum and Dad.

I was nervous heading down south, as I had no picture and did not know if my Dad would want me or hate me. Yet here I was knocking on his door. I was in my twenties and he was in his forties. I was dressed casually in jeans. The house was a reasonable semi detached on the corner of a street. Waiting, listening for telltale footsteps, I felt like running, but could not wait to see the man who was my biological father.

When the door finally opened, it was by an olive, tanned very dark haired man. His steely bluey brown eyes looking coolly at me, gave me a big shock. He half grinned and beckoned me in, Sandra came up the path too, and he waited for her, and led us into a lounge with a big settee, motioning for us to sit down. We both embraced each other with a cautious hug. "Sit down, please," he drawled in a laid back Canadian Cornish accent. I went over to the settee and sat, but immediately rose again as his wife came into the room. She was small with a big smile and very long straight dark hair. I gave her a hug, and she offered us tea or coffee.

It was a weird situation and I was a bit in awe. My Dad was well over 6ft and good-looking, he was a bit scruffy and laid back and half shaven, but he looked cool and like someone you would not mess with. He won you over when he grinned at you with his steely blue and brown eyes.

We talked and chit chatted about everything and nothing. He explained he had a daughter and a son both younger then me, and then he had divorced and brought his kids up single-handed. He had recently met his wife who I was meeting now. Some uncanny things were; he loved Alsatians' and wolves, and I did, and I had always wanted a guitar, and had one, but could not play it that well. He played the guitar really well, and was actually a lead player and singer in a band. He played in two bands as a hobby. The time flew, and we agreed that I would visit on my own the next day. Just he and I would go out on a picnic and try to get to know each other better.

Sandra dropped me off at 10.30am agreeing to pick me up at 5pm. I walked slowly up the path, not having to knock on the door as he was waiting. He bent down to give me a kiss and I gave him a huge hug. I followed him indoors, making a fuss of the two dogs and said, 'Hi,' to Judy his wife. It was nice she had the same name as my first dog. She was lovely and made up a picnic for us both. He offered me a drink before we left and as she had put the kettle on, I accepted, although I really wanted to get out of the house and chat to him alone. I felt I owed Judy a lot, as she seemed to be the driving force and it was she, who had made him acknowledge the letter. She was very friendly. I was ok with her, yet felt I had to be on my guard, as it was a very new relationship. I went outside into their garden at the back. It was small, but well planned and pretty, just enough space to sit out and have a drink, and room for some pretty shrubs, and a few fruit or veg.

I could not help looking at the bungalow next door, because it was a huge coincidence, and my Dad had not known, until I told him. My real Mum's mum, my Nan, lived in the bungalow next to him. Her garden backed on to his. I felt awkward because I had hinted I would come and visit her, and she had taken me by surprise, telling me I should be happy with what I had. She had hurt me, and surprised me, as she had been very good to me. I had respected her wishes, yet had nearly broken them, by being with my Dad next-door. I decided on that occasion not to tell her I had been down, as she hadn't invited me, and I hadn't known when I accepted, and came down to see my Dad, that he would live so close to her.

I was conscious at the time of seeing my Dad, that my real Mum also lived a couple of miles away from him. I too respected her wishes and decided not to intrude. I finished my mug of tea and placing it on the round table outside, went to inspect the shrubs, having sold many plants at the shop, I was interested in what plants they had in this area of England.

My Dad beckoned, he was ready to go, and I shouted, "Bye," to Judy. Following him back through the house, Judy came with us to the front door and said, "Have a nice time," she gave me a kiss and passed a picnic basket to my Dad. He put the basket into the boot of his Audi, and I got into the passenger side.

"Right," he drawled, "First I'm going to take you to the Hoe, where you were conceived." I hid my shock at his openness. My Dad drove slowly and carefully, making a detour showing me the police station where he used to work, and the local beach. He then drove on towards Plymouth Hoe. He pulled up alongside the Hoe and showed me a green grassy area on a hill, "This is where you were conceived." He did not seem emotional about it, and I felt a wave of mixed emotions, thinking my Mum had been foolish, but I could understand how he would have seemed a catch. He drove out of the Hoe and started to tell me of a place not far from there, where the divers would go. He stopped at a few small locations on the way. At one stop he told me, I had another half brother called Tim from Nottingham. He then followed on, "I must have kids all over the place." I did not comment, as I was too lost for words.

He took me to a pretty location and climbed out of the car to open the boot, fetching a blanket from the back seat, spreading it on the ground. We were on a cliff top looking out to sea, and I could hear the waves in the distance, and the cry of seagulls over head. Every now and again, a wisp of sea salt stung the air. My Dad started to unpack the picnic basket. There were cheese and ham sandwiches, a couple of packets of crisps, a flask of tea, and a packet of chocolate biscuits. He unpacked the sandwiches and helping himself to one of each, passed them, and laid back. I helped myself, making a pillow with my coat. The sun was on my face, and I felt great lying down close to my Dad. I asked him why he was retired, and he explained that his arteries had clogged up, and they had to operate and move part of an artery from his leg, and replace one in his neck with it. It sounded quite serious, and he said it was high cholesterol, and he just had to be careful. At the same time, I could not think of anyone more laid back. He went on to describe his job, his love of Alsatians, and how his love of the guitar, had managed to get him into two different music bands. He wanted me to meet the other people in the police band, and I said I would come and stop a week. He also wanted me to meet Simon and Susan, his son and daughter, but did not want them to know who I was. I respected his wishes, as he had his own life, which I was not really part of, the same for my Mum and my Nan, my life was really with my Mum and Dad in Leicestershire, who had brought me up.

I came back from the south with a satisfactory feeling; I got on well with my Dad. I thought he was a strong character. I also felt Judy looked after him well, keeping him on the straight and narrow. I too, had mixed feelings. I had not told Mum and Dad, knowing I was keeping it from them to protect them. I would have preferred they had known, and would have been happy about it. Richard had been ok about it, and thought I ought to go down again for a week. I said, I would have to write and ask Judy first and decide on suitable dates.

I decided that I could not go away for a whole week, without telling Mum and Dad, where and why I was going. I chatted about it with Sandra and she thought that they should know. I desperately did not want to hurt them, but Sandra said they were old enough to know I loved them, and it was only natural that I should want to meet him. I did tell Mum and Dad and felt awful about it.

First, I went to see Mum who was in the kitchen, and told her that I had found out about my biological Dad. He was a police officer, had just had an operation, and had been seriously ill. I explained, because of this I had taken the decision to go and stay a week down there. Mum just said, "Do what you have to do." She did not sound happy about it or sad. I went down the garden path and went to see Dad who was working in the green house. Apologising profusely, I told him that I loved him more than any other Dad in the world, but I had to go and see my biological Dad, as he had been so ill, and told him of the dates I had in mind. Dad did not go mad or shout he just said, "I see," and carried on with his potting up. I came out feeling guilty.

It had taken three or four sessions to tell Andrea about my first meeting with my real Dad and one time, I just seized up and refused to continue. Now Andrea was interrupting me. "Why feel guilty?" She waited for an answer. I shrugged my shoulders, and replied, "I love my Mum and Dad, and I wasn't being fair."

"You did not ask for this Bridget and you did your best, remember that." Andrea stood up, "I have to go now, try and remember what it was like when you went and stayed for a week." She got up and left.

I did my usual routine of going into the kitchen with my nurse to get a drink. It was to be another week before I could continue to tell Andrea about my stay with my biological Dad.

The next Friday I was on the motorway and only started to have reservations when I was on the A38 between Exeter and Plymouth. I pulled up outside my Dad's just after lunchtime. I felt awkward, although he was my real Dad, he was a stranger. I left the dogs in the car and rang the doorbell. Judy answered, "Hi Bridget," giving me a kiss on the cheek she said, "What do you want to do about the dogs; do you want them to come in?" I could not leave them in the car so I nodded.

"You fetch them; I'll leave the door open."

I went back to the car and lifted the tailgate making sure I grabbed both leads. The dogs rushed me up the pathway and through the front door. I took them through the lounge into the corridor, and took their leads off. My Dad was sitting having a cigarette on the step. He stood up, "Hi," he said giving me a hug. I smiled and walked back in to fetch the tea Judy had just made, and walked back out with it.

I was grateful to Judy, she appeared to be the boss, and took great care of my Dad. I felt that Judy had encouraged him to write to me answering my first letter. She told me that Susan and Simon would be calling in later. She joked about Simon and told me he was a bouncer at the local nightclub. He ate 11 eggs a day and had broken their toilet seat twice. Susan lived with her boyfriend, but was close to our Dad and she had two Alsatians. I was quite shy and it was another weird situation. Judy explained that as Graham had brought both the kids up single-handed, he was worried about the effect I might have on them. She said they had talked about it and thought for the present time it would be better that I was just presented as a friend from Leicester. I was disappointed, but I realised that as Mum and Dad were upset at home, it could be upsetting here.

My Dad joked to Judy saying I was like a stray dog turned up from the kennels. Judy was nice and asked me many leading questions. I gathered from the conversation that she and my Dad had not taken to Sandra. They asked me about my life. I ended up chatting about most things yet I painted a rosy picture and did not mention anything bad from my past.

Judy had cooked a big casserole dish for the evening, and I had never seen so many potatoes, she laughed saying Simon would eat most of them.

The doorbell went just before 7pm and I waited nervously on the settee. A very pretty girl was the first to come in with blonde hair and blue eyes. She said, "Hi," and smiled and walked into the kitchen. The door shut and Simon came into the room, beefy looking and massive, yet he was not fat, most of it being muscle. He came over and gave me a kiss. Judy told them both I was a friend of hers. Simon too went into the kitchen and I could hear Judy and him teasing each other over the food. Susan brought the plates through and my Dad had gone out to the step to have another cigarette. Everyone had numerous teas, and coffees and we were all quite hungry, smelling the chicken casserole from the oven and the garlic bread. Judy was right about the potatoes, Simon did her proud and he had more potatoes on his plate than I would have eaten in a week.

I spent time studying both him and Susan, envious of their relationship with my Dad. Simon was fun and he let on at the last minute that he was stopping the night. Judy got in a bit of a flap as I had taken his room. I offered to sleep somewhere else, but Simon said he would sleep on the settee in the lounge. Susan made a fuss of Jena and liked Jazz. She said I would have to meet her dogs. Judy laughed, explaining Susan had a small mini and both her two Alsatians sat on the back seat. Susan asked if I would like to go with her in the morning to the local beach with Simon and her two dogs. I told her I would love to, but felt apprehensive.

The next morning, I sat in Susan's car with both her dogs, and Simon filling the front seat. I sat cramped behind the drivers seat as he had the passenger seat full back. It was strange being with my half sister and brother and knowing we shared the same Dad, and not telling them who I was. Susan was friendly and some of the questions were awkward and too close to home. I had to lie or avoid, and all the time I wanted to cry out and say, "Your Dad is my Dad too," I could not and it was painful. Then I would remember who changed my nappy or looked after me if I fell over, it was not their Dad, it was my Dad. I brought myself back to reality by thinking of Mum and Dad back home. When Simon teased me, I rose to it and teased him back. We both enjoyed teasing each other, and I felt I could have got to know them both well. Time went fast and soon Susan was dropping me off, I felt like asking for her number, but did not. It was up to my Dad to tell them.

Back at my Dad's he told me about his time with the police, a couple of tales were horrific, one was when a lady covered herself with petrol and went crying into the police station, saying she was going to set herself alight. My Dad laughed, telling me, "I was on duty, I turned round and passed her my cigarette lighter," he drew on his cigarette smiling. "She didn't use it, I knew she wouldn't." I was not smiling, as I thought about the consequences if he had read it wrong. Then he continued, "Another story was between the Devon police and the Cornish police, there was a bridge separating the 2 counties, and this particular day a chap threatened to jump off, it was a popular site for suicide jumpers. I and my colleagues were just going off duty and we asked the guy to walk to the other side before he jumped as it wasn't in our area," he was laughing, he told me "The guy did, he walked across the centre to the other side and then he jumped." I could not see any funny side of this and if anything, it made me feel sick in the stomach. I felt sorry for the person, yet I felt sick that any human being could laugh at another ones pain. I wondered if my Dad had felt sick at the time and this was a defence. Overall, I knew deep down I loved my biological Dad, he was a genuine person, yet we had different morals and principles.

The next day Dad took me to the village hall, he told me it was his mates practice night and they played together. I had met some other friends who he had played and sang with at the other pub. These mates were his work friend, a Police *band. They were practicing here at the local hall and Dad introduced me to them. I liked them a lot.*

Dad played the lead guitar and shared the singing with another person called Roy. I enjoyed the music and promised I would watch them that night. I did watch them, being roped in to carrying the equipment and setting it all up. Judy enjoyed it and when my Dad had a break, she and him danced together. Their friends sat at our table. The woman called Lesley could not take her eyes off me. "I can't believe the resemblance," she nudged me again, "You are the same as Susan, you are a dark version and she is the light."

I smiled politely, she had been nice all night. Later, getting out of the car in front of the house, I felt everything going black and I collapsed. It was only for a short time and Judy helped me into my room. She thought I had drunk too much. I did not correct her; I could not explain my past.

Andrea interrupted, "I think you should have told her, it might have helped you." I shrugged and continued.

I was fine in the morning and Judy wanted to take me to a place called Dragon Mills, a retail outlet offering goods at very competitive prices. I bought loads of shrubs for my garden, and she bought loads for herself too. The car looked like a mobile jungle. Later I helped Judy put some shrubs in her garden. During this, Jazz decided to make an escape through the gate. I ran after her, she ran into my Nan's adjoining garden. I crept under the bay window whistling Jazz, terrified Nan would look out and see me. I called Jazz again and pretended to run away, it worked, she ran after me. I attached her lead and headed back to Judy, so relieved, telling Judy all about my Nan. Judy was sticking up for me, saying I had every right to visit my Dad and I should not feel guilty.

We had a lazy afternoon as Dad was doing another gig with the police band. He had gone to bed for a rest. Judy sent me up with a drink for him and I was touched to see a photo of me next to his bedside.

Andrea exclaimed, "Really?" and smiled.

The place of the gig was about 20 miles away. We followed the van, helping to load up speakers, and electric equipment. Dad tuned his guitar testing the microphone out. Judy fetched drinks for everyone from the bar. I was on orange juices, although I had insisted I had not been drunk. The songs were mostly country and western.

The next day Simon came and stopped, and I had such a laugh, I did not want him to go. He was rude to me and I was to him, yet it was all in good fun and Judy was laughing too. Simon went in the afternoon.

Judy, Dad and I went to a local pub. On the way home, I felt a bit carsick and decided to sit more forward. Judy was driving and Dad sat in front of me. Leaning forward to look out, I immediately did what I did to my own Dad at home and leant forward on the chair linking my arms around my Dad's neck. My real Dad did what my Dad did at home, reached, and touched my hand. For a couple of seconds it was special, and then out of nowhere, "Get off him." I still did not get it. Then the car braked to a halt and Judy turned round from driving, her face full of fury, again she said, "Get off him." I immediately retracted my arms and sat back on my seat. My Dad succumbed like a puppy, and I went to bed feeling miserable. I did not want to upset Judy at all. I was very conscious after that, if my Dad sat near me or I sat close to him. Judy did not mention the occasion again and I think she knew I received the message. I still was not sure if she had had too much to drink, or was very possessive. It did not add up as she had encouraged our friendship. Apart from that one incident, Judy was good to me and if it had not been for her, I don't think I would have been reunited with my real Dad.

She was also a very practical person and gave me some sound advice. One of the pieces of advice was to join a dating club. I had not taken her that seriously, yet she got me to write down ten things I would look for in a man and a sort of checklist. I wrote kind and caring, good sense of humour, genuine and honest, the list went on. She also asked a lot about Richard, and I did reveal that I was in an awkward position, and that sometimes I slept with my goats in the shed, as he would come to the window without warning and stare into my house. Judy got the message I was not dealing with him too well. She could also see my predicament in keeping it from Jane. She wanted to send Simon to sort him out and threaten him to behave.

The next morning Judy had a chat with me, she and my real Dad wanted me to go to the police about Richard. I was shocked. Judy explained that if I saw the police they could probably just give him a warning. She made me promise I would sort it out. My Dad agreed with her, "Look Bridget, when you go to the police station, ask to speak to a female officer." I sat at the table sipping my coffee slowly, I was thinking they were overreacting, yet Richard was becoming more and more obsessive about me. "Ok," I said to my real Dad, "I will go if it becomes worse."

Andrea asked, "Didn't it feel good, someone else knew and cared?"

I shrugged my shoulders, as at the time I did not take anything for granted.

My time at Judy's and Dads was ending and I enjoyed it and did not really want to go home. Yet I knew it had not been easy for Judy and she had been good to have me there, we were picking all the bags again for another gig. Dad ruffled my hair as he went past me to go upstairs, I grinned at him. I really wanted to give him a hug yet was aware of boundaries.

The weather was decent and Dad suggested taking me to the Hoe. I went with him in his car, and we got out and sat on the Hoe looking across at the sea. The white tips of the crests of the waves, made patterns in the sunlight. I took a deep breath, I loved the sea and it was one thing I missed being in Leicestershire.

My Dad searched in his jacket pocket for a cigarette, and clasping his hands, tried to light it. Helping, as although sunny, it was breezy, I put my hands around his, and for a second I had that magical moment and he looked into my eyes. Then it was gone as quick as it came. I lay back on the grass feeling the sun on my face, and the smell of tobacco merged with the salt in the air. He sat there looking out to sea. He stubbed the cigarette out on the ground and got up. I stood up and followed him and we made our way back to the car. He drove back and I sat in silence thinking.

I slept well, getting up early to leave to miss any traffic. Judy helped me with all the plants and we laughed as the dogs poked their noses through the jungle. The car looked steamed up already. "Take care," Judy said and she hugged me and went in. *My real Dad turned to me taking a chain off his neck, "Look Bridge," he said, putting it over my head. I held it and looked at it. It was a real gold chain and had the Star of David on it, for a second I wondered if I had Jewish blood in me, as I still did not know a lot about my background. He spoke before I could assume anything, "I haven't anything else of value, a lady friend gave me this when I was in Israel," he was laughing. I smiled; I was not going to change him. We hugged and I said, "Bye and thanks." I got into the car, tears in my eyes; I started the engine, driving slowly. Once he was out of sight, I put my foot down. I felt so churned up. I drove as if I had never driven before, far too fast. As it was so early, I hardly passed any other cars. When I got home, I let both dogs into the garden and I ran to ring my biological Dad. He answered the phone. "Hi," I said*

"Hi. Where are you?" he said

"I'm home," I replied sitting down.

"No seriously, where are you?"

"I am home, if you want ring my number or do a check afterwards."

"Crikey!" he said, "Take care."

"I will and thanks," I put the phone down, I looked at the time, I had done Plymouth to Leicester in two and a quarter hours, no wonder he didn't believe me. I felt as though I had driven with all the tension from the last few days.

Now I felt lost. I took my bags upstairs and then I went to look at my animals, it was only as I started to look at my animals that I realised how good my animals made me feel. They did not cause hurt or grief and there was no catch. I could be me and no one else.

Andrea looked at me. "Is that really how you felt?" she asked.

"Here, I am not supposed to tell I am adopted. There I am not supposed to be the real me. How else do I think?" I replied. She shrugged hard. She did not have an answer.

Dr Lynn was quite pleased with the progress I had made. I thought he would suggest a relief off level ones, and a possible break at home. I was mistaken. He decided to ask me to continue to relate to Andrea after returning from seeing my biological Dad, how it affected me, if at all, when I returned home. I felt embarrassed. Yet I found it easier to talk about chronological events then specific incidents. It was easier as I was like an automatic robot relating without thinking too hard. Andrea sat back in the comfortable armchair with her coffee, and I lay back propped up on the pillows on my hospital bed.

I was a bit subdued, still thinking of what Judy and my real Dad had said about talking to the police. I decided to try to talk to Mum and Denny first.

I drove up Mum and Dad's drive, bringing them some shrubs for the garden. Mum was pleased to see me and gave me a big hug. Dad was not back yet, as usual, Mum was in the kitchen, and she put the kettle on. "Mum," I hesitated again, "Mum, I need some advice, and I don't know what to do." Mum continued to pour the tea, and I knew she had heard me, but had not replied, "Mum, I'm having problems with Richard, he keeps telling me, he's married the wrong sister, and won't leave me alone." I took a deep breath. I had said it.

Mum passed me my cup. She still did not say anything. "Mum, I don't know if I should tell Jane," I sat down at the table and put both my hands around the cup as if to draw comfort from it, it did not help. Mum sat down and after taking, a sip of her tea replied, "Of course you can't tell Jane, tell him off, he's only messing about." She made it sound so easy, "Mum, I have told him, he thinks it's funny, he..."

"Sssh, here's your Dad." Mum glared at me and I stood up to say hello to Dad as he walked into the kitchen, he came over and gave me a kiss, "How's my No 2 daughter?"

"Fine," I got up to show him the shrubs I'd bought for them, both him and Mum liked the ceonothus which had bright blue flowers. I had also bought a red pyracantha, which had lethal spikes but would look good along the garage wall, and clematis, which was a flowering climber for the wooden fence. Dad seemed pleased, but soon sat down and disappeared behind the paper. Mum was busy with his dinner, so I left.

That evening, as I half watched the television. I browsed through a magazine and came by chance, across an advert that took a whole page by Dateline. I remembered what Judy had said and wondered if I should give it a go. I started to fill the questionnaire in. I sent the envelope off the next day with a cheque. I rang Tina up and told her what I had done, she called me a dare devil, yet she was excited.

CHAPTER 8

Dateline

Richard was getting worse. Soon I was unable to be anywhere private with him, without him coming on to me. He would laugh and joke and the trouble was he knew I would not tell Jane. I rang Denny up and she told her husband. She rang back and said, "It's no good, you will have to pack your job in." I thought hard about that, and had many sleepless nights, Sandra knew he was a nuisance and she called him all the names under the sun. In addition, I knew he was messing about with another barmaid.

I was in a mess; if I gave up my job the chances of another was not good. I had a long sick record. Judy rang to see how I was doing and I said, "Fine." She did not believe me and asked directly about Richard, I found to my dismay I could not speak. She could tell, "Please go to the police station, you can't live like this," she said.

"I tried to tell my Mum," I said, trying to defend why I had not gone to the police, "What did she say?" asked Judy.

"She didn't take it seriously and she told me whatever I did I mustn't tell my Dad."

"Shit!" said Judy, and I was surprised to hear her swear, "You go to the police now, do you hear me and you ring me back later," she hung up and I screwed up my face in disbelief,

"Oh shit," I muttered to myself. I put the dogs in the back and got my coat. I drove to the police station and went into the little waiting room. It was a good half hour

later when a young policewoman turned up and asked me to follow her to a side room. The sight of her uniform made me want to go, as I did not want Richard to get into trouble. "How can I help?" she asked, and I looked down at the floor, unable to speak. Then I started to explain, "I am working with my brother in law and he is a really nice fellow, but I am starting to have problems with him trying to kiss me..." hesitating, I felt I was not explaining properly. She smiled and I explained that I could not stop in my lounge in my own house, as he would creep up and look through the window from outside. She was writing things down and then she looked up, "Has he hurt you?" It took me by surprise and I frowned and said, "No," not sure.

She asked another question. "Has he threatened you?" Again, I did not know what to say. Richard had told me, he wanted me and no one else was going to have me. Yet it was not a proper threat, again I said. "Not really, he keeps saying no one else will have me but he hasn't done anything, look my real Dad's a policeman down South he told me to come and see you, they thought you might be able to warn him off me. I don't want him to get into trouble, I just want some help."

She smiled and stood up, " I can't do anything until he does something to you; the best thing you can do is to tell him you have seen us, that we have his name on our records, and warn him that you will come to us if anything happens." She was holding the door open; I thanked her and walked to the car. I was relieved I had done it, but it did not seem to have got me anywhere. I went home and rang Judy up.

"Hi Judy, it's me I've just got back, I spoke to a policewoman."

"Good girl, did they help?" Judy asked,

"No, not really she said they couldn't do anything until he did, but I can tell him that I have been to see them and try and warn him off."

"Well that's better than nothing," said Judy.

"Great," I said, "He'll love me, what if he stops me working with him?"

"He won't, not if he wants you that much, come off it Bridget look at all the advances he's making at you, anyway knowing how sick he is he'll probably find it funny. I still think you've done the right thing, look love I've got to go, ring again."

"Bye Judy." I put the phone down, now what, how could I tell him I had just been to the police to tell on him. I went next door to see Tina. She was sympathetic.

Again I didn't sleep well, I was wondering whether I should have told Jane, or if I'd done the right thing, I rang Sandra up she was well pleased and said he needed reporting. Yet she could see my predicament and at the same time was sympathetic. She told me to have a word with Richard, "Tell him the truth you never know Bridget, he might get the message and leave you alone, things might get back to normal."

The next morning Richard was making the coffee and I was at the desk sorting out the mail. I said, "I have something to tell you." I had a knot in my stomach and was now wondering whether I should have told him when we were in a more public place. "What now?" said Richard putting my coffee on the desk. "I've been to the police and told them about you," for a second he looked white and went really quiet, "I didn't want to, you gave me no choice, you won't leave me alone." I felt bad and guilty; he stood with his coffee not touching it. "We've only had a laugh, I've never hurt you, I didn't deserve that, and you could have talked to me," he was not happy. "I did talk to you and I've asked and asked and you just laugh," I said.

"Well they can't charge me for tickling you, can they, and what else have they got, and if they were going to get me they would already be here." He turned away and went back to the engine bit he was working on. I put my coffee down and carried on. I was feeling really mixed up. Richard was quiet for the rest of the day and we hardly talked. It did not make me feel better, I felt miserable.

I decided to go round to Mum and Dad's and tell them that I'd been to the police station about Richard, Mum wasn't there so I decided to tell Dad. I kept putting it off, as every time I looked at him, Mum's words rang in the back of my head. "Whatever you do don't tell your Dad." Yet I needed to and yet I could not, after idle chatter I virtually gave up and rose to give Dad a kiss on the cheek. "I'm going Dad." I said, he put the paper on the table and got out of his chair, "I'll walk down the drive with you and open the gates for your Mum," he replied. As we walked down the drive, I turned to him and said. "Dad I have something to tell you."

"What's that love?" he said, bending down to pull the catch up on the gate to swing it open. "Well it's not nice and I don't know what you'll think, but I have been having problems with Richard, he keeps going after me saying he's married the wrong sister. I have not ever encouraged him but it got to the point where I could not cope at work. I was advised to go to the police to warn him off."

Dad looked shocked, "The police, what the hell do you need to go to the police for? I'm disappointed in you, why didn't you come and tell me first?" He was angry, but not with Richard, with me. "I did come here for help. I asked Mum, she told me not to let you know, he wouldn't stop."

"Well, I am ashamed of you; Richard helped you get your mortgage and gave you a job." He walked up the drive with his back to me. I felt pretty awful and turning from him, I walked to my car, got in, and drove home.

When I got in I made some microwave chips and fried an egg, I had no energy to do a better meal. I had just finished and was washing my plate and rinsing off the ketchup when the phone rang. "Hi," I said, thinking it would be Judy. "Is that Bridget?" I did not recognise the voice and answered back puzzled, "Yes. Who's that?"

"Hi, this is Andy, I'm from Dateline and received your details, and I thought you might like to meet up." I nearly dropped the phone.

I agreed to meet him next Friday at 8pm. He told me he would have a green jacket on, and I did not give any info, he knew what I looked like from the details when I registered with Dateline. Later I looked at my post and found correspondence from the agency, Andy's details were on there. I went round to see Tina and took the paper with me, she was laughing like mad and teasing, "Where are you meeting?" she asked, "As if I'd tell you, you'd come and watch," I answered back grinning. "Get there early, sit in your car, watch and if you recognise him, and he looks awful go," said Tina. "I couldn't do that, I'd have to see him and get away early," I said.

She wished me luck when I left her house. I did not tell anyone else, Mum and Dad would not approve, and for another reason I did not want Richard finding out yet.

On Friday, I decided to go smart casual. I did go early and I sat in my car, I questioned myself what was I doing, for my heart was racing, and I was scared stiff. I didn't see anyone go in with a green jacket. I took a deep breath and walked slowly to the pub. Inside it was rowdy and smokey. I was just wondering whether I should go and order myself a drink, when this jovial sort of guy came up, extended his hand and said, "I'm Andy," I shook his hand and smiled at him, and he beckoned me over to a table, "What would you like to drink?" he asked.

"Just a coke thanks, but I'll get the next drink."

As he stood at the bar, I studied him. He had casual trousers and a baggy shirt, long greasy dark hair and a sort of stubble. He came back, passing me a coke, and sat opposite. I found out he drove a forklift truck and his favourite football team was Coventry. As much as I tried to keep a conversation going, I found him boring. He had borrowed his Mum's car to get here; he still lived with his Mum, his argument was, he could not see the point of moving out and cooking for himself, if he did not have to. I found myself time watching and wanted to disappear, but I felt I owed him a drink, so drank my first one quickly to get another one in quick.

He liked to talk, but it was about his mates, the football team, and the pub near him. I stood up after I had finished my second drink, and told him I did not want to be late as I had an early start. He did not ask about seeing me again and I was so thankful, I said bye and walked quickly to my car. I was shaking when I got home; glad to get into bed, thinking I would ring Judy the next day. I did but it was to tell her, I thought I had made a mistake. She was not having it, "Don't be daft, he's the first, you're bound to get some bad ones as well as good, have a laugh out of it." I did not feel like laughing and for the next couple of days I was jumping every time the phone rang.

Andy didn't ring again, but another guy did, his name was Bill, and I agreed to meet him in Sileby at a local pub. Tina wanted a full update, on how the date with Andy went. She wanted to know who Bill was, and where I was meeting him. It was nice to be able to chat with her. I did not tell Sandra, as I knew she would not like it either.

When I waited in the pub car park to see Bill, I was again very nervous. He was already there in his van, and I felt myself blushing, as I knew he was watching me, as I parked my car. He got out of his van and I got out of my car quickly. He came over and grinned. He had a nice grin, yet he was very scruffy and a lot older than I was. "Hi there," he did not offer to shake hands but had walked quickly to open the door for me, I went through and he followed, we both walked up to the bar together. "And the lady wants…" Bill turned to look at me.

"Just a coke thanks," I said. Bill had a pint and came over to the table where I sat on a cushioned bench, "Do you mind if I join you on that?" Bill asked. "Course not," I moved so that there was plenty of space between us. I quite liked Bill, he was very chatty, and he made me laugh. I could not see him as a potential partner but he was ok as a friend. He asked outright in the car park, if we could meet again, and I agreed and said the following Wednesday, same place same time.

That Wednesday he was there again in his van waiting, this time as he came towards me, he had a bunch of flowers. He passed them to me grinning. I said, "Thanks," a bit sheepishly, and put them into my car.

"After the lady," he said following me into the pub.

He still had the same jeans on with a tear across the knee, a long shirt hanging on the outside and trainers. He told me he was a postman and made me laugh with some of the stories he told. We got on so well that night that I let him know my address, and he volunteered to help me move some heavy planters, the next Sunday afternoon. Tina was well excited and kept singing the Postman Pat song.

Sunday was bright and sunny and I tidied up a bit. I hoped Jazz would behave herself, yet Bill was used to dogs, he had laughed when I told him I had Jena and Jazz. "It wouldn't be good would it, a postie scared of dogs?"

The doorbell went at dead on 2pm and I opened it to let Bill in, I put my head round the door to look at the front of next door but there was no sign of Tina. Bill came in and followed me through to the outside. Both dogs barked, he picked up a nearby tennis ball and threw it, Jazz immediately responded by bringing it back to him and they were friends for life. He wanted to see the goats, so we went to see Bluey and Snowy first and fed them some carrots. He then went into the chipmunk aviary fascinated by them coming up to him and sitting on his hand feeding. We were having a good laugh, and were just moving this planter between us when we heard the Postman Pat song, it was Tina leaning out her back window with her daughter singing Postman Pat, but with Postman Bill instead. "You sod," I mouthed behind his back to her laughing. She was laughing like mad and so was Bill.

We disappeared inside to have a cup of tea and Bill started working in the garden again, when my door went. I thought it was Tina and opened it. I was shocked to see Richard. "Hi," he said, "Stick the kettle on." He walked past me into the garden, as he usually played with Jazz, and stopped suddenly at the sight of Bill. "Who's that?" he said scowling.

"Hey Bill," I shouted, "Come and say hello to Richard, my brother in law,"

Bill came over smiling, "Hiya Mate," he said, "Doesn't she work you hard!" He winked at me; Richard ignored him and looked at me, "Who's Bill?" he asked again. "Bill's, Bill." I said shrugging my shoulders and Bill smiled at me. Richard turned and went and fussed over Jazz, I could tell he was not happy, and I had been shocked as I thought he was down South. He got up and came over. "I'll pick you up at 7.30am." He put his empty mug down, nodded to Bill, and went. Bill said, "He doesn't seem too happy."

"Ignore it," I said. I knew Richard was fuming, but was glad in one way he had seen me with someone, Bill helped me a lot, and I said I would see him at the pub on Wednesday.

The next morning I was waiting for a response from Richard. He surprised me and turned up in his Ferrari. It was a gold one and quite old but was in good condition and Richard being an engineer had it tuned finely. "Bill's, Bill," he said, looking at me, "What's that supposed to mean, where the hell do you know him from?"

I turned to Andrea, "That's when he drove me into a wall." I said.

She looked carefully at me and I knew she could tell I was shaking. "You already told Dr Lynn about that incident didn't you?"

I shook my head. "Not properly, that was the one you wanted me to write about and I couldn't, I gave basic details."

Andrea looked at me, "Well carry on talking to me about Richard's reaction to Bill." I took a deep breath remembering when I got into his Ferrari.

"He's just a friend," I said looking at him as I climbed onto the luxury leather seats and placed my bag at my feet. Richard started the engine and accelerated fast. He continued to drive fast through the streets and headed for Leicester. Once

on the dual carriageway, he opened throttle and we sped past other cars at a *frightening rate. We were approaching traffic lights and I clung on to the door handle, he showed no intention of slowing down. They changed to red just as we approached, he went straight through them the car wheels screeching as he took the sharp right bend. "Do you know what?" Turning he looked straight at me. I could tell from the glisten in his eyes and the croak in his voice that he was deadly serious. "If I can't have you, then no one else will."*

I did not answer but clung to the handle as he increased his speed, swearing violently, reaching 150mph. He turned sharply up a side road and headed across some derelict land straight towards a brick wall. I closed my eyes clinging to my seat belt thinking this is it. Suddenly he swung the car and the back end hit the wall. There was a crash as the wall buckled and the smoke and dust swirled. I was thrown and jolted, and felt the impact through my body, yet I was still alive. Richard looked across at me saying, "If I can't have you, no one else will." He then drove to the unit.

Inside I was shaking yet I was determined not to let him see he had got to me. That day, work was horrible and I was glad when it finished. I also thought things through, and although I knew I did not want Richard and that Bill was ok, I felt the agro and hassle I would receive for just being friends with Bill was not worth it. I knew deep down that Bill was looking for more than friendship. What he wanted, I was not prepared to give."

I looked at Andrea and stared defiant as if daring her to challenge me. She did not and actually said I had done enough and needed a break. She rose and told me I had done really well. When she left I felt really agitated and desperate to get out. I outwitted the level one nurse. I was unstoppable. I ran across the hospital car park and by chance bumped into Alison. She laughed when she saw me. "What are you up to?" she asked. I felt rebellious and she had a bad influence. "I need to go somewhere, do something different."

"Well come on then, let's go." She started to walk off and I followed her. I knew I needed to get to a motorway or railway, or even my favourite place the quarry. "How much cash have you got?" Alison asked.

"Enough," I replied.

"Let's catch a taxi, go on ring, I know you have a card, I saw it on you before." Alison egged me on I had some money and we hired a taxi to the nearest motorway service station. We sat at the table inside and had a coffee. I was too restless to drink and walked to the glass corridor over the motorway. From here, I could see the bridge nearby that had a small road leading up to it. I walked quickly down the steps and headed for the road. Alison followed me shouting, "What the fuck are you doing?" I ignored her and started to walk up the steep lay-by up to the bridge.

Once on the bridge I started to walk towards the centre. By this time, Alison had lost all the toughness in her voice and sounded quite scared. "What the fucking hell are you doing, get back here?" I ignored her, staring at the volumes of traffic passing under me. I started to look where I could climb over, busy concentrating on the most suitable gap to climb on. I was not thinking rationally, my main aim was to climb the fence. In the background, I could hear Alison talking and did not really cotton on whom she was talking to. She suddenly ran up to me, handing me her phone. I automatically put the receiver to my ear. "Bridge, Bridge what are you doing?" I could hear Clare's voice on the phone, she was one of the zaniest nurses I had met, but she was also very good and caring. I still did not ground myself; focussing on which part of the fencing to jump over. The bridge actually had one sort of barrier and then a sort of smaller one just under. I answered truthfully. "Hi, Clare, I am looking for a piece of fence to get on to." Behind me, Alison was now starting to scream hysterically, she had gone from a toughie to a cowering wreck. "Bridge, can you see a police car?" Clare spoke with urgency but calmly. I looked round I could see one coming over the bridge, its blue light was flashing but silent. My attention for a second drawn to the car; its occupants drove by us at a slow rate and pulled up a few yards away. "Yes, one has pulled up a few yards away."

"Bridge, what are the people in the car doing?" I looked across to the car to answer Clare's question. Two police officers had climbed out of the car; the driver was talking to Alison. She was still screaming hysterically. The other man had started to walk up the slope and across the bridge, towards me. As he drew near, he suddenly stopped. I looked away from him and down towards the zooming vehicles below. "Hey!" He called. I looked at him and he hesitated, then called again, "Hey, it's Bridget isn't it?" I nodded, looking towards Alison who was still standing with the driver. Just at that moment, Clare interrupted, "Bridge, Bridge, what's going on?"

"Police are here, wanting to talk." I said, staring across at the young officer who was walking at a slow pace towards me. "Hey, Bridget, your friend is very worried; you don't want to scare her do you?" He called. I looked towards Alison who was staring across the bridge at me. I shook my head, I could hear Clare saying, "Listen to the police, they're trying to help." I looked again towards the young man coming towards me. "Bridget, your friend here thinks you need some help, is she right?" He stopped in his tracks only a few feet away. I could hear Clare on the phone asking what was going on. I ignored the phone and looked at the police officer.

He was only young probably in his thirties; he had blondish hair thinning on the top and bright blue eyes. When he smiled, two dimples lit his cheeks. I looked back from him towards the gap in the fence and suddenly felt very sick. What was I doing here on top of a motorway bridge, I could not recollect how I had arrived in this position, all I wanted was to get back to my room and ring the kids up. I did not move I could hear Clare still asking someone to speak to her. I held out the phone to the police officer. He moved cautiously over and took it from me. I could see him listening but had no idea what Clare was saying to him. He was still within arms reach from me and I still made no move. He eventually clicked the phone off and said. "Well do you want that lift back to a nice warm reception with a cup of tea? Your friend said if we hurry now she will talk to you when you get back." I nodded and moved slowly with him across the bridge to the car.

As I approached the car, Alison ran up and hugged me, "You little fucker," she cried, "You scared the fucking daylights out of me." I slowly got into the back of the police car. Little did she know how bad I felt. I had nearly killed myself and it had been unintentional, there was no way I wanted to die. I sunk back onto the car seat; I wanted Joseph and the children. I was firmly back to reality and grounded. Arriving back at the hospital, I felt embarrassed, thanked the police officers, and gave Clare a sheepish grin as I made my way back to my room.

I had a bad few weeks and attempted to jump out of several windows, each time worked up, unable to see past the initial reaction. I was like a volcano ready to erupt, and the minor eruptions each time caused a crisis. I would try to get rid of the feeling but it would build and build, and finally I would lose control, acting out impulsively. Usually, I would grab the nearest item that I could do damage with, and often it would be a coffee mug innocently sitting there. I would make a desperate dash for it and smash it on the nearest available surface, lashing out at myself using the sharpest piece. The rush of cutting knocked out the pain. My bleeding arms would then give me release from the awful pressure that was destroying me. The downfall, it was only a temporary release. Other times I would make a dash and the staff would be in hot pursuit, I would target the nearest available item. I never planned these occasions, and sometimes the nearest item would be a window and I would smash my way through with the first blow. The windows were supposed to be safety ones, and when smashed you could see the double layer with the enforcer in between. The problem was my adrenalin was at full pelt and I was so focused my strength was enormous.

At school, I had beaten most of the lads in arm wrestles. In hospital, my own strength became a lethal weapon against myself. Once I had decided to go, a single nurse was unable to hold me and it took several to restrain me. After the adrenalin rush, I was fine and often apologetic. I never intended for these attacks to happen. Sometimes I would feel the build up and look for the release before it epitomized. I would start to strangle myself by obtaining any cord I could get, including dressing gown belts, stockings, tights, or someone's jeans belt. I would take the nylon cords off around the bin tops. I had a store for when needed.

When well, in between these stages, I never got rid of these stores; to me they were my safety. They were my release from the distress and pain I would suffer, when these build-ups happened. My level one watch definitely saved my life and protected me at times, although at other times when I could feel the build up happening, I was desperate for them not to be there, as I needed to break the cycle. I would then turn to being devious and still self-harm behind their backs or make a bolt. I would take the first opportunity that arrived. When Miss Nasty had called me an opportunist, she was correct to an extent. I never planned an opportunity but if I was unwell at the time, I would be looking for the first available one that came, anything from cutting, strangling running or any other way out.

If I bolted and managed to get away from the immediate surroundings, I could still be on a high from the enormous wave of adrenalin rushing through my body, and I could run straight across a vehicles pathway, to just heading for the most dangerous surroundings I could think of. Once I had calmed down, I would ring the ward. Sometimes I was aware that I was in danger from myself and would ring the ward for help.

Andrea and Dr Lynn were now eager to press on. Andrea asked me to continue to relate to her, how I dealt with my life after Richard had warned me of his intentions, with the fast ride in the Ferrari.

"I ended the relationship with Bill and he took it badly. I could not go into detail why, and I felt bad about it. I met a few other guys from the dating agency, but with respect to them, I could see why they had been left on the shelf. One guy could not stop moaning about how everyone ignored him, and how his work colleagues missed him out from parties, and how no one would talk to him. I tried, it was impossible, he was so self absorbed I felt like putting a mirror up where I was sitting. I kept to my personal morals and was polite enough to stay for the

drink, but was so glad to escape. I did see an accountant for a while, yet he spoilt me, and put me on a pedestal.

Matthew was a strong character, he was a butcher from Leeds, and at first, we got on really well. Then he held back whenever we went out, and I ended up paying. I did not mind going Dutch especially when I did not really know someone that well. Yet I was not happy at paying for everything. He was tall, lanky and quite good looking until he smiled. He had awful teeth, and I ended up ditching him. I breathed a sigh of relief. I was coming fast to the conclusion that I did not want anybody, when the phone went. I picked it up and said, "Hello."

A foreign sounding voice said, "Bridget?" At first, I thought it was my cousin from Belgium, as he had the same sounding accent.

"Hi," I replied. I was never good at putting on a phone voice. I believed in being myself, and people either accepted me or did not.

Anyway, this person introduced himself as Joseph. I listened and was so hooked, I missed Emmerdale, and the telephone conversation stretched from a few minutes to nearly an hour."

Andrea smiled and said, "This is so romantic." I laughed throwing my pillow at her. "Don't stop," she said, leaning back in her chair, using my pillow as a cushion.

"When he had finished, he rang off promising to ring me again. He told me he was Swiss and worked at a very exclusive gourmet restaurant in Rutland. Excited by his phone call, I went rushing round to Tina next door to tell her about him. We sat and giggled. He told me that he would send me the latest catering magazine, where there was a double page on him. In return, I promised to send him a photo of myself. I actually sent a photo of my two goats as a joke, and a small one of me behind them. He did send the magazine, and I was not sure how I felt when I first saw the photograph of him, yet I liked his moustache."

Andrea laughed. I grinned, "I always have liked men with moustaches, put it down to a misled childhood watching Magnum."

CHAPTER 9

Joseph

"The next day, I took the magazine to show Mum and Dad, who I was still very close to. The article was very impressive and described the job of a wine sommelier. Mum and Dad were somewhat interested. They always made jokes about me being left on the shelf, as both my sisters were married. I showed the article to Richard. "He's just a glorified waiter," he said. Then he called him 007 James Bond trying to run away from somewhere. Joseph had worked at a top restaurant in Hollywood and three star Michelin restaurants elsewhere. He was a wine expert and his job was to advise people which wine went best with which dish.

However, Joseph did not ring and after a week, I went round to Tina feeling miserable and she told me to ring the hotel up and ask for him.

"I can't do that, what if he hasn't rang me on purpose? He might have taken one look at the photograph and said no thanks."

She laughed, "Don't be mad, he would take one look at you and say yes please. Go home and ring him."

"I can't, he might not want to talk to me."

"You'll never know if you don't try, go on, go home he might have lost your number, and go on home to think about your phone call, ring him."

I went home, looked the number of the hotel up, then I made a cup of coffee and sat down. I was a true coward and did not dare ring. Then I thought of our conversation, so I rang and asked for him. The girl on the telephone was very *friendly saying she would try to find him. My heart was beating like mad, and my hands were all sweating. I kept expecting her to say he was busy or not there. Then he answered. He kept apologising, saying he had lost my number and had rang many numbers, never getting the right one. He was laughing and so was I. He asked if we could meet, he apologised saying he had no car but could meet me in Leicester. I knew in my heart straight away that he would want somewhere better than the local pub. I desperately tried to think of a close venue and suggested The Grand Hotel. He agreed but suggested I met him at the train station, as he had no clue to where to go. We would meet early at 6.30pm, due to the train times.*

I arranged with Mum and Dad who were visiting Denny in Oadby that night, to drop me off at the railway station, and pick me up at 9.30pm, as he had to catch the 9.15pm back anyway.

After the telephone call with him, I was so happy I went running round to tell Tina all about it, I also told her the next night I would be meeting him.

I did not dare tell Richard. I decided to go smart and wear a short black skirt and black jacket with a white top. Mum and Dad could not believe I had a skirt on, it was unheard of, and I suffered the jokes all the way to the train station. I also heeded their warnings of not going off alone with him. I assured them I would be at The Grand Hotel and then at the station for 9.30pm.

They dropped me off just before 6.30pm, and the loudspeakers announced the arrival of the train from Peterborough. I waited back nearer the exit, and I saw him before he saw me. He looked small, wearing baggy brown corduroy trousers and a green jacket. He had mousy coloured hair, and a rather big nose and a moustache. However, he looked quite becoming when he turned round and smiled, having two very deep dimples and an impish grin. He strode across to me as if he was a soldier on parade, very straight back and a purposeful walk. I took a step towards him and smiling said, "Hi." He enquired if I had been waiting long. I shook my head, and we strode out of the station towards the area of the hotel. He walked quite fast, and I was skipping to keep up the pace. We both seemed shy and it was a lot harder to converse. I was thankful when we arrived at the hotel. He held the door open for me.

We both saw a sign together, which said Simon's bar and headed for the stairway. Once at the bar he asked me what I would like to drink, thinking he was the professional expert and not being a big drinker, I told him to choose. He suggested champagne, and I laughed thinking he was joking. He was not, and five minutes later, we were heading for a worn leather sofa, each with a glass of champagne.

When we sat down, I desperately tried to keep the conversation going. I joked about needing a telephone each on the end of the sofa, and he laughed. From that moment on, we sat and talked about anything from the weather to the condition of the sofa.

As we finished our glasses, he suggested we went for a meal. He said he had had nothing to eat. We booked ourselves into the hotels restaurant, sitting opposite him; he talked mainly about his brother. The waiter offered me some bread and I took a roll conscious of how to eat it. Some told me to cut it with a knife, others had told me it was not polite and you had to tear at it. I played safe and waited for him to start on his. He tore a little off and I did the same. I chose steak well done, much to the potential disgust of the chef. He chose steak rare and I tried not to look as he cut it with the bloodiness trickling out. He laughed at me. I liked the sound of his brother who liked dogs and was into photography. Joseph was well into food and wine. We were so opposite. He was well accustomed to city life, smart restaurants and finery. I preferred a more down to earth country style with animals and nature. I liked his manners and his sense of humour, his foreign accent, and the fact that he was Swiss. He laughed at the goat photos and was very complimentary. We arranged to meet the following Sunday, where I would bring the dogs to Rutland Waters.

Finishing dinner, I glanced at my watch, well aware Mum and Dad would be worried if I was late. It was nearly ten o' clock. I jumped up panicking, telling him I must get to the station quickly. He was also worried, as he had missed his last train home. He insisted on paying for the meal and we both left. We ran most of the way and when I got to the railway car park, Mum came over, upset and very angry. "Where have you been? Your Dad's not taken his insulin, he's looking for you," she hardly glanced at Joseph. I apologised trying to calm her, "I will look for Dad," I guessed he would have gone to the platform Joseph was originally going to go from. As we walked through the hall, Dad came towards us. He looked angry. "Where have you been, I've been worried sick!" I did not want to say eating a meal having a nice time. "Sorry Dad, I lost track of the time." Joseph stepped forward interrupting, "Sorry it's my fault." Dad looked at him, "I thought your train was going earlier."

"Yes, I've missed it, don't worry I shall catch a taxi." Joseph smiled at me, I had no chance for proper introductions as Dad was rushing to the car. I leaned, and putting my hands on his shoulders gave Joseph a quick kiss on the cheek. "See you Sunday, ring, sorry, bye." I ran off leaving him staring after me. I jumped into the car with Dad and Mum. Dad drove quickly towards home dropping me off, I apologised all the way back.

Tina laughed when I told her about the disaster of the first night, "Poor Joseph that's a good start," she was happy I liked him, and told me to have a good time that Sunday.

I went round to Mum and Dads to apologise again and they had calmed down. I explained exactly how Joseph had unexpectedly invited me for a meal, and that I was sorry we did not keep a better check on the time. Mum and Dad apologised, explained they were panicking as Dad had not taken his insulin, expecting to be home earlier.We all had a cup of tea and they were quite excited that I actually seemed keen on Joseph. I told them I was going out on Sunday and taking both dogs. Dad laughed, "Poor lad," he said as he got up taking the newspaper with him, "He doesn't know what he's letting himself in for."

Sunday was cold but bright. I took both dogs onto the back seat of my car, which had an old rug on it and headed off for Oakham. I had instructions where to pick Joseph up, and he was then, directing me to the area of RutlandWater. I drove through Twyford and Burrough on the Hill to Somerby. Now I was approaching Oakham and once over the railway track, I headed straight down the main street. Joseph was waiting on a corner. He smiled as he got into the car and I reciprocated. Both dogs were very good and did not even move. Joseph directed me to a small roundabout where I took a left turn to head towards RutlandWaters. He took me to a remote car park, and it was nice as with no one about I could let the dogs off.We continued on our walk chatting about the other night. I was embarrassed, as both my parents had been shouting. Joseph was apologetic. I assured him both Mum and Dad apologised and that they were just worried for me and because Dad had not taken his insulin.

The sun came out, the dew on the grass glistening. We had a lovely walk, both Jazz and Jena were good, and we relaxed. The man-made lakes looked clear and the odd flash of a fish appeared now and again. Joseph told me he was going to come over and visit me when he could. He worked really long hours and had no car. He arranged a night off and decided to stay Sunday night, if I could get him to the station for the 8.30am train on the Monday. I agreed as I could drop him off on the way to work. I told him I would cook a meal and he arranged to be at Leicester station early Sunday afternoon. I had to go and pick him up.

It was a week away and I felt sorry that I was not going to see him. Joseph said he would miss me but would try to ring. I joked, "That's if you can find my number." He laughed and grabbed me towards him, drawing me close, we had our first proper embrace. Our mouths parted, I felt the roughness of his moustache on my skin, his hands tightening on mine, and I squeezed his hand back. We walked slowly back to the car. I did not want to go, but knew I had to drop him off at the hotel, as he had to work later that day. As he jumped out, he shut the door and leaned through the car window. "I have had a beautiful time, I will look forward to seeing you on Sunday," he waved. I drove off feeling happy, already wondering what to cook him, for his meal.

All week at work, I was looking forward to Sunday, Richard did not know, I did not tell him, and I managed to shut out any sort of feeling when he tried to trap me or place his mouth on mine. He still would not believe that one day I would not be his."

Andrea who appeared settled and nearly falling asleep startled me by asking me if I was worried about Richard finding out. I told her, what would be, would be, quite casually. Richard would not stop me from seeing Joseph.

"The weekend came and on Saturday, I went to see Sandra and told her I had met a Swiss guy and was cooking for him. These days Sandra was not so possessive and *actually suggested I do an easy bread crumbed turkey steak with fine chips and a salad. She suggested a mixed cheeseboard for afters. I also bought fresh orange juice for the morning and a selection of jam to have with toast. As I did not drink, I did not think to buy a bottle of wine.*

Sunday morning I tidied up the house and had a sandwich at lunchtime. I put both the dogs in the conservatory and headed for the station. I hoped Joseph would be on time. He was and came over with a small sports holdall. He put it in the back, and jumping into the passenger seat gave me a kiss on the cheek. I set off to get my prized possession home as soon as possible. I was nervous pulling on to my driveway. I had a nice two bedroomed semi detached house, yet I so wanted Joseph to like it. He was lucky because when he arrived most of the work had been done, and it looked nice in the lounge and both bedrooms were fine. I was not sure about the sleeping arrangements, but playing safe, I put Joseph in the big bedroom where Jazz slept and I kept my bedroom to myself. I thought it was a good way of checking his intentions.

Joseph came outside eager to see the garden and the goats, he came and looked at the rabbits and chipmunks. He liked the ducks. He was not keen on the dogs being able to sleep on the chair on their rugs, and I tried to compromise by putting the dogs onto the floor.

We had a relaxing afternoon, drinking tea and lazing together on the settee talking. Tina came round for half an hour and Joseph laughed and joked with her. "He's gorgeous," she whispered as she left. I grinned shutting the door."

Andrea spoke, "It's amazing how detailed you can be about Joseph, yet when I ask you finer details about Richard or the vet you can't remember."

I shrugged my shoulders. "I am only telling you how it was," I said. I continued to tell her about Joseph. It was easy as the details were clear.

"Joseph beckoned me over to him, and as I leant to kiss him, he pulled me down and we both fell to the floor laughing. We kissed and hugged and both of us respecting the other, got to our feet to sit on the sofa and watch the TV. "I will

start the dinner," I said. He wanted to know if I wanted any help, "No, I am fine, sit back and laze," I suggested. I peeped in after 10 minutes, and he was fast asleep on the sofa. I left him, as I concentrated on the dinner, and it was not until half an hour later, when I woke him for dinner. Joseph had bought a bottle of wine so he opened that, and we sat and enjoyed a nice meal. After, he loved the cheese board selection, and we curled back up on the settee with coffee. He respected my decision of sleeping in the guest room, and he did not try to come in through the night. I was partly disappointed yet happier that he respected me.

We were both up early in the morning and Joseph was happy with toast, jam, and fresh orange juice. He had a coffee, I had a tea, and it was time for him to go. Just before we left the house, he took my arm and turned me to face him, "Look, I have had a lovely time. I am sorry I have already had this booked; I go to Switzerland on Tuesday for two weeks to see my family, but please think about this. I would love to move in and live with you." He leant and gave me a kiss, "Please use this time to think about it." I was in shock. I had not known him that long. I was sorry he was going to Switzerland, but it also gave me space to think. I nodded, "I'll think about it and it's a big compliment you like it so much here." He smiled.

I dropped Joseph at the station and carried on to work. Richard asked me why I did not want a lift that morning. I hesitated then thought I have nothing to hide, "I had to take Joseph back to the station," he grimaced turning away to the grinding machine. I went and put the kettle on; I was not going to give Joseph up.

Later Richard came over to me. "It's him or me," he said. I was shaking but I hid it and just ignored him. The next week Joseph went back to Switzerland and Richard asked me to go to the accountants on the motorway."

"You know what happened," I said turning to Andrea.

"Yes and I don't want you to repeat that," she replied frowning.

"I don't want to repeat anything at all," I said.

"I know, it's hard, but we are making progress, you may not see it, and it will take time," Andrea said. I lay back on my bed and sighed, this seemed never-ending.

When Dr Lynn visited me, he told me that he wanted me to continue to tell Andrea what happened after the car accident. I shrugged my shoulders, I was bored of telling them about my life, and it seemed an intrusion of privacy where Joseph was concerned. Yet I made another effort and the next morning started to tell Andrea about the weeks after the accident.

"The police had told me, I had to take my driving documents into the police station within so many days, and Tina said she would take me. I had seen my GP and he told me to see him again just before the 2 weeks were up, so we could review the situation. Tina was like a guardian angel, coming round and dragging me back to hers. She was a couple of years younger and already had two children. We watched the morning TV and she told me she would take me to the police station the next day. I had a nightmare that night and woke up wet through. I kept seeing a baby thrown from a car on the motorway, and car after car smashing into mine. Then between that was Richard laughing and his face was behind bars but when he pushed, the door swung open.

I got up early again and could not eat anything, I only drank half my tea and went and looked at my car documents and driving license. I put them into my handbag, went, and let the dogs out. The other animals were fine; Tina had been coming and feeding them. I had not heard from Joseph and hoped he was having a nice time in Switzerland.

When Tina came for me at 11am, I was a nervous wreck. "What's the matter with you, you're not on trial, all you have to do is give the documents in," she opened the front door and I followed her out. I still had a job to look around properly, as my neck collar restricted movement. I clambered into the front seat of her Jeep and we set off, the police station was only down the road so I did not think we would be long. I felt worked up, stressed and tired. Tina drove into the car park. "I'll wait here I am looking at some properties look," she showed me a local estate agents paper and had circled some houses. "You're not moving are you?"

"Well, not straight away but we are looking for somewhere bigger," she looked apologetic. "Oh, I had no idea, I'll help you look." I was at a loss for words. I

walked off towards the police station. When I walked inside, I felt dizzy and sick. Tina's words had shocked me as I realised, I leant on her a lot, and I was still thinking of whether I should say something about Richard. I looked up expecting to be alone and to hand my documents in. Unfortunately, there were two other people in front both sitting waiting. I sat down and hoped they were together. It was soon apparent they were not and I leant back against the wall. It was another twenty minutes before the police officer came back to the desk and luckily the next person did not take long. I walked up as soon as they came away, and he smiled and apologised for the delay explaining they had some travellers out the back and it had caused a few problems. I gave him my driving documents, and after answering a few questions finished.

Feeling relieved, I wished I had ate some breakfast, as I felt sick. Walking across the car park, I looked up at Tina's car, she was still looking at the property magazine, and I hoped she was not too late to pick up her kids from playschool. I lifted my hand to knock on her window, suddenly my legs buckled, and the last thing I remembered was hitting my head on the side of the door as I went crashing to the floor. I vaguely remember hearing a scream then I was out of it.

I heard voices and it was children singing in the background, "You're dead, you're dead, we'll kick you in the head." I tried to open my eyes but they would not open, and then I was looking through blades of grass, I could see feet approaching and hearing someone shout. I heard Tina's voice saying, "It's your fault you shouldn't have made her wait." I could not keep my eyes open, I slipped into oblivion. Someone was holding my hand, and as I tried to look up, the police officer from the reception bent over me, "Hello, the ambulance will be here in a minute love, has anyone got her coat?" I felt a coat placed high covering my face. "Don't bury me yet," I said and Tina half laughed. I squeezed the hand holding mine, it was comforting. I tried to look to see who or what was happening, but had no energy and could not open my eyes properly. The ambulance got louder and louder as it approached. Someone was talking to me and I tried hard to pay attention but was unable. The ambulance men were putting a straight support behind my back and were strapping me in. They had talked to Tina. I was falling into blackness, vaguely aware of a mask placed onto my face, and then lifted into *the ambulance. One of the ambulance men kept chatting to me. He put something onto my finger, and tried to get me to follow his finger, asking me how many fingers could I see? I would have answered yet could not keep my eyes open.*

I was aware of being transferred from the ambulance trolley onto the hospital trolley. A nurse took some details and both ambulance men said, "Bye," I tried to smile and nodded to them. I had to do some tests. A doctor came in and shone a bright light into my eyes. He told me I could not go until they had done some further x-rays. I told them how bad the tingling had been in the shower. The doctor told me I needed more rest and prescribed some stronger tablets. He told me my body had had a shock to its system and needed time to readjust and not to rush things.

Tina picked me up and was brilliant, she even had a word with the nurse and when we arrived home, would not go until I was tucked up in bed. She took a spare key.

She was extremely good to me for the next few days and made all my meals. I felt worse and very tired. Richard appeared at the front window one day and I jumped, as I was not sure how long he had been watching me. I had to let him in. He asked when I would be back at work and I said I did not know. He made him and me a cup of tea. I was uneasy with him and glad when he left. That night I woke up and could see Richard staring at me through the lounge window. It took me ages to convince myself it was a dream. In the morning was a piece of paper through the door. I made out the words, 'If I can't have you, no one...'

I went and sat in the goat shed with the goats. I did not want to sit in the lounge until I knew he would not be there. I wanted to pull the curtains but then wanted to make sure I could see that no one was there. In the end, the goat shed was more comfortable. It was only halfway through Josephs stay in Switzerland, and suddenly I felt that I could not cope or did not want to. I was unable to picture the future; all my feelings were belonging to the present time.

I suddenly had an intense craving for something to take the pressure or distress I was feeling away. The pain was enormous, and as I walked through the conservatory, I saw an empty milk bottle. I wanted it to rip my stomach open; I was not thinking of the consequences, I just wanted the pain to stop. The way I saw it, was a distraction. I had no strength to plunge the bottle into me. I thought if I fell onto it, it would cut me open. I held the bottle to my side falling heavily onto the concrete slab, the bottle hitting it first, with my stomach resting bare onto it. It would not break. It made me feel even more desperate and frustrated. In the end I smashed the bottle on the floor and picked up a sharp piece of glass, without hesitating I plunged it into my thigh. It ripped straight through my jeans, slicing through my flesh, and the edges were white like pork, before it coloured with blood. The pain did its job, taking my mind off the present feeling, and I did a few more cuts, which sort of gave me a high and rescued me a little bit."

I looked at Andrea. She was grimacing and pulling a face. I continued trying to remember the exact details.

"I then decided I was ok enough to walk down to the nearby newsagent and buy a paper and some chocolate. I needed desperately to escape from myself. I went out and walked slowly down to the shop. On the way, I again started to feel bad. My thigh hurt and I felt faint. I abandoned plans to get a paper or chocolate, I picked up a can of coke thinking the sugar content would help me out. Walking up to the counter I collapsed and the can fell to the floor.

The darkness started to lift and I could hear voices, someone was bending over me saying I was a good actor. I was so scared and embarrassed, I did not dare open my eyes, and then I felt my nail being, painfully pinched. I switched, I was in my world; where people could do anything, and it did not hurt protected in my bubble. The voice said, "She's tough." I felt myself lifted out in a chair and still I kept my eyes shut. I was not here they could not hurt me. They were lifting me into an ambulance and the voice said, "Ok you can open your eyes now."

I opened my eyes I was in an ambulance with two young ambulance men. "Come on love, the show's over, tell us where you live and we'll take you home." One of the men half smiled.

My mind was blank. I was panicking and my leg was hurting like mad. I could not think straight. I was thinking of Susanne and she lived in Grantham. I was thinking I had £2 in my pocket and that was all. "Come on love where do you live?"

I muttered what was on my mind, "Grantham," both men looked surprised as they looked at each other. "Well we can take you back there," they started to move. One of them shut the door and the other turned to me. "What's your name love?" He asked. I shook my head.

Strapping me in, he accidentally brushed against my leg and I winced, as it was extremely sore. The other man moved over quickly, "Hold on," he said, and as they both looked at my jeans, they noticed the tears in the material and the blood. They swung my legs round up on the stretcher bed and before I could say anything or object. One of them was undoing my jeans and the other was already pulling them down. My thigh looked a mess; there was a big piece of flesh jutting out in a triangle. The other places had bled, causing the bloodstains on the jeans. They both looked at me, "How did this happen?" The older one asked, and I replied quietly, "I fell on a bottle in the alleyway."

"Alleyway?" all I could see was an image of a green bottle in an alleyway. I was in a sort of denial. The next thing I knew, they were radioing the hospital telling them they were bringing me."

Andrea was nodding as I was relating what happened.

"I lay back not caring about anything. I was in need of serious help but at the time could not see it. They took me in to hospital and kept asking me my name, I kept saying I did not know. They wheeled me to a small side room and a nurse came in to ask me some questions. I kept looking at her blankly. I kept saying Grantham. They pulled my jeans off and took my top off replacing them with a hospital gown, telling me my leg-needed stitches, and cleaning.

Wheeling me onto a ward, I had to wait for a psychiatrist. This scared me and when the nurse disappeared, I pulled the curtain back from around my bed and spotted my clothes on a chair. I dressed quickly. Opening the curtains I watched, once the nurse went the other way, I jumped off my bed and headed down the corridor. I had no idea where I was going, but needed to get to the outside. I passed an official looking desk and headed for the exit direction. I looked behind me and realised a young nurse off my ward was following me. I quickened my *speed and then coming towards me, was shocked to see the head of the ward. He approached me, "Hello where are you going?"*

"To get some fresh air," I whispered.

"Ok, you are coming back, aren't you?"

I looked at him. I was not, but now I felt trapped, as I never lied. I changed my mind as the way he was looking if I had said no I would have been in trouble. "Yes I won't be long." He looked at me intently,

"I shall see you back shortly?"

I nodded and went out the door. I was in the area where the ambulances came in. I stood back and watched, although I felt distanced off. The two ambulance men who brought me in arrived back. They both were nice and tried to tease or trick me into giving information. I could not, I genuinely did not know. I headed back.

It was late evening and I had had no drink or anything to eat, when a small Indian Dr came and introduced himself. He asked me questions, which I could not answer. I felt I needed to tell him some answers and could only think of Susanne's name so told him, her name and Grantham. I could not say anything else, he told me he would be back later, but was thinking of admitting me to another hospital. I panicked and told him not to take me anywhere because I would jump from the ambulance or run away. He went and sent a nurse to be with me. If she had not been there, I think I would have disappeared.

She asked me lots of questions and things started to ring a bell. The psychiatrist came back. He pulled the curtains around the bed and sat down on a chair, "I found the medical records of Susanne, and rang the telephone number on the records. Her father answered and gave me her present number, which is in the Grantham area. I rang this number and managed to talk to her partner. He tells me that Susanne is there with him and you are Bridget her best friend; you have been best friends since the age of five. Is that right?" He was staring at me questioningly, and I felt weird. It was as if he was a long way away, yet part of me knew he was sitting right next to my bed. I looked at him and was not able to verbalize but just nodded my head.

He wrote down some notes, "How are you feeling now I've told you your name?" I shrugged my shoulders. I wanted to talk but was unable. He turned and looking up from his notes said, "I am going to admit you to another unit across Leicester." I jumped up wincing as my leg hurt. I had forgotten about it. I had been there hours, no one had cleaned it, and it was now a mess of black congealed blood still with this white piece of flesh sticking out. "Please don't, it's coming back to me, please don't I'll try to escape, I'll leap from the ambulance I won't stay wherever, please let me go home." I was grabbing my pillows as if my life depended on it. He looked at me and hesitated. "Please," I begged but could say no more.

He sat back tapping his pen on the note pad, "Well the only other option is if I let the ambulance take you home, you promise to report to me at this address at 10am in the morning. He looked at his watch, it's already after 1am, if you go straight to bed at home and then report to me, I'll let you go." I leant back relieved. He stood up, "I'll give instructions for an ambulance team to see you into your home, I will see you in the morning," with a courtesy nod he had gone and the curtains wafted back and forth.

It was a good hour or more later when the ambulance team arrived. It was a woman and man. They were nice and jovial. I had dressed back into my clothes and still had an untreated wound. I did not dare say anything, as I did not want stitches. Once home they walked me inside. I could hear Jazz barking in the conservatory, but happily knew that Tina would have been round. Since the first time I was ill she had decided to check in every night. I had initially protested but she had said, "You never know," and deep down I knew she was right. I said bye to the ambulance people and went to make a quick drink, as I was cold. I stopped mid track from the lounge, as I could not remember where my fridge was. I knew about the dogs, I knew where to put the kettle on. I searched desperately, the kitchen was too small, and it was not in the pantry store. I went into the conservatory and found it placed near the sliding door. I took out some milk and made a cup of tea. I was so tired I put the milk away, gave both the dogs a biscuit, and took my tea upstairs. Again halfway, I halted, as I was not sure where I was heading. I undressed and got into bed, my leg was still a mess, I did not care, it was nearly three in the morning, and I was shattered.

The next morning Richard turned up early, I had forgotten he usually called *to see if I was going to work. I told him I had an appointment with this Dr at ten o'clock. He kept asking me why and I would not say except that I had been in hospital the day before. He kept asking what I had said and I kept saying nothing. He insisted taking me and as I had no clue, where we were going I was partly glad of the lift. Yet I was scared of Richard.*

Once there we drove into a small car park and I walked up to a dismal looking building and through the doors. Asking at the reception where to go, Richard still insisted he accompanied me. We headed down a corridor into a ward. There were three nurses at a desk and a small office on the left. I gave the card with the appointment written on and was led to a small lounge. Richard accompanied me and once we sat down, he jumped up and started to pace the room. He got more and more agitated and I got quite scared. Telling him I needed the loo, I walked out to the desk. I was desperate for the loo, but even more desperate to tell someone not to let Richard in the same room as me. I approached the nurse on the far end of the desk, as the other two were talking. "Please, I need to go to the loo is there a toilet nearby?" She started to tell me to go out down the corridor, when she was interrupted, "No, it's fine for you to use the ladies on this ward, straight down there on the left," an older woman had pointed the directions to me. I thanked her and took the opportunity, "Please, can you pass a message on it's urgent, please tell the Dr, I don't want my brother-in-law in with me, please don't let him in?" My voice had cracked and I was pleading. The nurse put her hand on my arm as if to reassure me, "Don't worry, we'll pass the message on." I smiled and followed her directions to the toilet.

When I came out the Dr had arrived and Richard was hovering on the ward outside the door. One of the nurses guided me back through to the room, asking Richard politely to wait on the chair on the ward. The Dr smiled at me and asked me to sit down. I was extremely nervous really wanting to bolt, yet Richard was on the other side of the door. As we tried to engage in a conversation, Richard kept looking through the glass panel. The Dr was nice; he asked me what had happened when I got home. I explained I could not remember everything. All the time I kept looking at Richard, pleading with the Dr, not to let Richard into the room. The Dr looked uneasy, and he too made a remark as Richard was again pressing his face on the glass looking through. He turned to me, "Look we aren't going to get very far with your brother-in-law here; I suggest you come back next week and see Dr Pagely." I nodded so relieved to get out, yet I felt like I wanted to scream and tell him that I was scared of Richard.

He gave me another card with the next appointment and shook my hand. I thanked him and walked out. Richard was asking me before I was through the door, "What do they want, what did you say?" Once out I headed towards the lorry, "I have to go back next week," Richard grunted as he walked round and opened the driver's door. He pushed open the passenger side, and crashed the gears twice before we were out of the car park. I was in turmoil feeling lost and tired. Richard drove me home and he followed me in. He went and put the kettle on and made two teas. I sat down and he came and passed me a drink, "Watch these quacks," he said. "They are no good, you'd be better without them.""

I said it very quietly, but embarrassed as I felt the comment was rude. Andrea just laughed, "No wonder, he warned you off. He was scared what you were going to tell people."

"Not a lot happened that week, I knew Joseph had been asked by his work to visit a few vineyards in France, after his visit to Switzerland, so was not coming back when planned, but a fortnight later. I had not told him what had happened, as our relationship was new and I did not want to concern him. I was still not sure whether to let him move in, yet my gut instinct kept saying yes. Mum and Dad were still away in Australia. Susanne had telephoned to see if I was ok. She was shocked that I had been in hospital but I reassured her I was fine. I promised I would ring her if I needed her and after went outside to see the animals.

The next day I drove with extreme care to the hospital to see Dr Pagely. He asked me about my memory loss and queried the black outs. I told him I worked with Richard and was under a lot of pressure. I kept silent, when he asked personal questions. My mind seemed to go blank and I sat uncomfortable in my chair. He told me it was hard for me to open up to a stranger and appreciated that it would be difficult. He asked me to return in a fortnight, and I rushed through the dark waiting room to get outside. The building itself was depressive. The windows were all similar and it looked more like prison cells than a hospital. At home, I made myself a sandwich and wrote down on my calendar, the next appointment date. It was in the first week of April. Mum and Dad returned from Australia and Joseph was back the next week. I did not tell Mum and Dad I was still seeing a psychiatrist.

I decided to check Mum and Dads reaction to the proposal of Joseph moving in. "What do you think of Joseph moving in with me?" I looked from one to the other, preparing for a battle, as Dad was very old fashioned, and I knew he would object. Their response especially his, blew me sideways. "When, do you want a hand with his luggage?" He lifted his cup to his lips and took a sip of tea before placing it down. I looked at him gone out. Mum said, "If you don't mind me asking where's he going to sleep?"

"Where do you think, in the goat shed?" I made a joke of it on purpose, as I was offended. "No seriously, he'll sleep in the spare room with Jazz."

Both Mum and Dad laughed, "Poor lad." Dad said again, he had a soft spot for Joseph and I was still shocked at his reaction to help him move in. I finished my tea, "Well I've got to go, just thought I'd keep you up to date." I disappeared and headed for Sandra. I had my own keys still, so let myself in. I wandered through the lounge, which stunk of cigarettes to the kitchen at the back. Sandra was at the sink washing some net curtains. I gave her a peck on the cheek and sat down. "Hiya stranger," she said and automatically reached and put the kettle on.

"What have you got to tell me then?" She asked.

"Joseph's back tomorrow and I have to make a decision whether to let him move in." I hesitated, waiting for her to reply. She did not and I looked at her. Since I had my own place, she had let go of the apron strings. She lit a fag up and I hated it, as she blew the smoke out facing me. "Whatever I say, you will do what you want, so most likely your decision is already made." It was true, as I knew I was going to let him stay. I finished my coffee with her and left. The dogs had enjoyed being together and it was nice to see her. Yet she had changed a lot towards me.

Joseph arrived back mid afternoon the next day, I knew instantly I was happy to see him and gave him a big hug. He gave me a big parcel in a carrier bag with the Swiss cross on it. "Undo it," he said, excited, and I undid the bag and pulled out what was inside. It was a rucksack black and cream made in Switzerland from genuine cows hide. It had the Swiss emblem on the catch. I leant forward and gave him a big kiss recognising this was not a cheap souvenir. Joseph took his coat off and sat on the settee telling me how his parents were, and what a good trip it had been. He then asked me how I had been, and I hesitated, I did not really want to let him know I had been as bad as I had. "I had a slight car accident and have severe whiplash, and because I lost my memory temporarily due to the accident, I still have to go to the hospital." I said it rushed, and he looked at me intently. I did not mention Richard and I did not mention the psychiatrist, just briefly explaining. "Are you ok really?" he put his arm around me and I grinned leaning onto him.

"Well I could have been better, but Tina's been fantastic and things are getting back to normal." I passed him his tea and started to drink mine.

I told him later that I was happy for him to move in, but he would have to contribute to the rent, and Mum and Dad were ok about it too. Joseph looked happy. "That's good," he said, "I will fetch my things at the weekend," he laughed, when I told him Dad was jumping at the gun to go and help him."

Andrea said, "After all the things that had happened to you, you would let a nearly complete stranger move in. I do not understand you yet Bridget. I would have thought that you would never meet anyone in a pub who you did not know, and as for letting some stranger move into your house. I sometimes find you unbelievable."

"Joseph moved in at the weekend and Dad really did go and help him fetch all his belongings. I was apprehensive, yet happy. Tina thought Joseph was lovely and encouraged the move too. I was sad, as she and Mark put their house up on the market. I went back to the hospital several times and saw Dr Pagely. Each time I seized up and could not talk about personal details. He eventually told me that

he was leaving and moving on to another area in psychiatry. "Who do you want to see?" he asked looking at me. It was nice he gave me the choice. "Do you want to see my replacement or the top man himself?" He was grinning waiting for a reply as he held his pen ready. "What do you mean the top man?" I asked.

"Well he is the consultant and we all work as a team, but he more or less leads it."

"I might as well see him then." I said, thinking if I saw the top man, he would probably say I was fine and dismiss me.

Joseph was fine about me coming to the hospital and I suggested reluctantly I did some more part time work for Richard, as we needed the money. Joseph's article in the magazine had led me to believe he made a substantial sum of money a year. I found out, he actually, earnt peanuts and his contribution to the house, took most of his money. He also worked long hours having to go at 7am in the morning to get to the restaurant and then most nights he would not be home until 2-3am in the morning. He had some of Sunday off but had to return for the evening shift. I told him to demand a pay rise. He did do this, his boss helped him finance a car yet not at the cheapest of rates, and agreed to a pay rise. This helped a little but we were still struggling with the bills.

It was nice to have Joseph at home although I hardly saw him. I tried to encourage him to take more time off, yet he was passionate about his job and conscientious. I finally told him about Richard. How he had threatened to kill me. I told him that the car accident was deliberate and how if I had gone on the motorway I would not be here. I warned Joseph that Richard had called him a glorified waiter who was running away from something. Joseph was quite mature about it. He laughed and told me not to worry, but there was no way I would be working for Richard again. My Dr also told me with the whiplash injuries and because of the recent blackouts and memory loss, he was not prepared to sign me off the sick.

I started to try to write freelance and wrote a few pieces on animals accepted for magazines.

Joseph liked his food, being fussy, liking only the best quality. This was a bad combination when we were trying to save money. Yet he had worked at La

Gavroche, one of the best Michelin starred restaurants ran by the Roux brothers. He had also worked at L'Orangerie in Hollywood, where he had lived for 5 years. Here, teaching many of the celebrities about wine and food. He had helped set up a wine club in California and was used to the high life of the best food and wine. He had won some prestigious awards for the best wine cellar for the restaurant where he presently worked in Rutland. I was very proud of him and he showed me some further magazines and books that featured him. The Mail on Sunday did a whole page on him the following week and Dad started to tease him asking for his autograph."

Andrea said, "Autograph no, bottle of wine yes." We both laughed.

"It was Josephs' 30th birthday and I had secretly arranged a champagne trip to Reims for a long weekend. Tina had said she would look after my animals. Joseph had taken the 4 days off, aware we were away, not knowing where. Susanne and Tom were coming with us and Tom was driving. It was fun. I had sneaked Joseph's passport into my bag and packed what we needed. Mum and Dad were in on the secret, and everyone was quite excited. It was early when Tom picked us up, and I knew the ferry went at 11am from Dover to Calais. Tom was a good driver and it was nice to sit as a passenger and relax. Joseph was guessing all the time. He first thought we were going to Cornwall as we headed south. Then he changed his mind to London, and then when we were on route to Dover, he was guessing Disneyland.

Susanne and Tom were laughing, all the way across the sea, he was still guessing, and it was not until we were on the main carriageway in France to Reims, that we gave him a few champagne clues and he guessed. He was excited, phoning several champagne makers, all sounding the best of friends to him and arranging some extra visits.

Tom and Susanne were enjoying the trip, Susanne was a quiet tall dark nice looking girl. She was very placid and gentle. Tom was 6ft 7 with very dark curly hair. It was obvious they adored one another, and Tom got on well with Joseph.

We checked into the hotel at Reims, and headed out to grab a bite to eat. It was very different than in England and we sat outside at a street cafe. In England it was easy to snack, here in France, they took food more seriously and the waiters described the food to the finest detail. We let Joseph take the lead, and he explained to us anything we had not understood from the waiter. He was so pleased and I was happy that we had made a good decision. We spent the rest of the afternoon exploring the area and window-shopping. In the morning we were to visit a local champagne maker, the trip was part of the weekend, and later on in the afternoon Joseph had arranged for us to meet one of his friends, who was a well known champagne maker.

We had a brilliant evening left late and in high spirits. I was a bit worse for wear in the morning but managed to join everyone in the breakfast salon. Tom had brought his map with him and Joseph who knew the area showed him the route to the champagne house. We were to arrive there by half past ten. We went back to our rooms to get ready. The champagne house was fun, a little train trip underground, very cleverly done. After, there was more tasting and a chance to buy. We declined knowing it was very commercial, preferring to sample the champagne in the afternoon at Joseph's friends. For lunch, we stopped off at a local farm restaurant and we all chose a light salad. Joseph was wearing a shirt that Tom and Susanne had bought him and they were joking to him not to spill anything on it.

Soon we were heading out through fields down narrow lanes, when all of a sudden Tom drove through some large gates with the name of the champagne house on them. The champagne maker came out of the house and greeted us with joy. He ushered us through to a large kitchen where his wife greeted us too. There were many stuffed wild animal heads, buffalo, bears, and several sorts of deer. Each wall had a head staring from it. I did not dare look at Susanne, as I knew I would laugh. She was a bigger softy than me, where animals were concerned.

We sat at a huge kitchen table on long benches. I sat next to Joseph with the champagne maker's wife on my left and opposite Susanne and Tom. His wife got up, and undoing a bottle of champagne continued to hand a glass out to each of us. We raised our glasses, "Salute," we said.

Joseph was in serious discussion with his friend. The time went by and the *empty clean glasses turned to drunken used ones. Suddenly the wife came back with an album and her husband eagerly gestured us to look. I expected it to be photos of champagne making. It was full of photo after photo of them on safari and the unfortunate shot victim and glory of the hunter. I initially grimaced but seeing how proud Joseph's friends were, smiled and passed the book to Susanne. By this time, the champagne had gone to my head and my smile turned into a loud laugh as I caught the look on Susanne's face. Joseph's friends mistook my laugh for enjoyment and she eagerly came over to point the trophies of animal heads out to Susanne. I was nearly hysterical, as I knew deep down Susanne would never have looked at them and I could see the funny side, as she was shown more and more.*

As time went by my hysterical sense of humour could not keep under wraps, and as I laughed and tried not to, I laughed more. The funny thing was that the wife was now laughing and every time I laughed, she was crying with laughter. I had tears down my face and Tom and Susanne who were usually so very polite and quiet were crying with laughter. Joseph and his friend looked on amused and his friend was clearly explaining the champagne was very good. We eventually left with gifts of champagne and glasses. Tom who had not drank too much was joking that he had never seen Susanne plastered, and Joseph was laughing at the state I was in.

Once back at the hotel I collapsed on the bed and Joseph went to make me a coffee. The weekend went too fast and we all promised we would go on another long weekend together as we had such a good time."

"See," I said to Andrea. "Joseph was a gentleman even when we all had a drink."

Andrea smiled. "I hope so for your sake," she said.

"When we got back to England; I had my first appointment with Dr Lynn." I said. "Tell me how you got on with Joseph," Andrea replied.

"We were getting on well and I was glad he had moved in. He had moved from the spare room into mine after three months trial with Jazz as a companion. Soon after he had moved in, he told me he had wanted to buy me a present and had

taken me to the pet shop and bought me two Dutch rabbits and a white chipmunk, who we called Houdini, as he escaped into the porch. Tina came to the rescue posting her husbands fishing hat through the letterbox for me to recapture him.

Every few weeks I went to see Dr Lynn, it seemed a very false environment as he would nod briefly if he did acknowledge you outside the room, and then talk freely inside the room. He did not just ask about my brother-in-law and my memory loss. He started to ask questions about my family, my childhood, and present situation. I found I could talk about the present situation. Each time I thought he was going to discharge me, he would ask me to make another appointment.

Time was moving towards Christmas and Joseph was busy at work. Fed up with him working so hard, I told him to look around for another job, where he would be appreciated more. We both tried the agencies and found due to the specialist expertise he had, jobs were not easy to come by. In the past both of us had been self employed and we agreed that this may be a way forward with Joseph acting as a wine consultant to Michelin starred restaurants, and any restaurant or hotel that needed advice or would benefit from a decent wine list. Joseph was adamant that quality would come first preferably from small vineyards leaving the big commercial producers to the big commercial outlets such as supermarkets. He was also very keen that the average person had access to his wines and decided he would also have private clientele, people who enjoyed a good glass of wine.

Joseph again asked to see his boss and eventually after threatening to give his notice in, he worked evenings only. This gave us the chance to set up our own business. We were both excited. Christmas, he had to work through the lunch having the afternoon and evening off. We had already told Mum and Dad we would come to them for Christmas, Denny and her young family were coming, also Jane and Richard in the afternoon.

Joseph was a little shocked at the traditional Christmas menu. At home in Switzerland, they had oysters, which made me feel sick, and then seafood and possibly a goose. He thought turkey with all the trimmings was boring. I could not have eaten any of his menus, so was glad I was in England. The only thought *attracting me to Switzerland in the winter, was the thought of sitting on a sheepskin rug in front of a blazing fire, in a log cabin up a mountain. Memories of my Mum sighing after watching Omar Sharrif in Dr Zhivago, reality checks of my Dad coming in from the garden.*

It was Christmas Eve and I was on my own. Joseph was working and I was doing some last minute present wrapping. Christmas at Mum and Dads was the usual, some presents in the morning and church if we felt like it. Christmas dinner, the Queens' speech at three, and presents after. Joseph was aiming for four o'clock and Mum was saving him a dinner. We agreed not to open the presents until he arrived. Jane and Denny were already there, I kept out of Richards' way. Joseph was on time, which was a rare occasion, and we all opened our presents. He loved my presents and I had a glowing feeling, as he hugged and kissed me. Now Denny was taking photographs. I was tired it had been a good day and I wanted to go home. Joseph and I left at ten pm after thanking Mum and Dad. I asked them up to us on Boxing Day but I knew Dad always went to watch the Tigers play.

This morning it was frosty and sunny and I tidied up, Joseph was working in the back room, gradually my house was changing into a wine warehouse. I was getting ready to see my GP. It was my regular fortnightly appointment. He smiled and asked me how I was doing, "Fine," was my regular answer even though it was apparent at times I wasn't. I had something to ask him, "I'm 35 soon, both my sisters say if I want children I should start to try now as it can take a couple of years sometimes?" I looked at him.

"Not always sometimes it can take a couple of minutes," he said laughingly, "No seriously, if you have the right partner and you want children especially with you having ME on and off then I would consider it." I left the room in deep thought. I was going to speak to Joseph. The next morning we both sat in the conservatory with fresh orange juice, toast, Joseph had a strong mug of coffee, and I had my cup of tea. He spoke to me. "My boss wants me to go to South Africa in February on a wine trip; I'd like you to come as well."

I looked at him gone out, "I wanted to talk to you, I want your honest opinion, I talked to my Dr, and he reckons if we want children we should start to try." I looked at him to work out his reaction.

"Well why not, I was thinking we could get married this spring or sometime this year." It was my turn to look surprised. We both continued to drink our drinks as if the conversation was an everyday one.

The following week it was my birthday, January 20, which happened to be a Saturday. Joseph still had to work but he had spoilt me again. I had a fantastic gold necklace with a small silver ring dangling on it with tiny diamonds embedded in it. I fell in love with it straight away.

January turned to February and Susanne's birthday was February 2, Joseph and I went to the local Thai Restaurant where Susanne was meeting her parents and her brother. We joined the party and after I gave her a bag full of goodies to open at home. We had been best friends for thirty years. She looked well and happy. The meal lived up to expectations; we all left in a contented mood.

We arrived home just after midnight, and Joseph and I curled up together in bed. "I ought to ask your Dad if I can marry you," he said scratching his chin thoughtfully. "Well you could ask me first," I said laughing.

"No, because if your Dad says, 'No' then there's no point is there?" he looked seriously at me, I frowned and propping up my pillow I said, "Are you going to tell him we're trying for a baby at the same time?"

"Ok, ok," said Joseph, "I get the picture, we will get married this year whatever your Dad says, and hopefully we will have his blessing."

"When are you going to tell your parents?"

"Not until they need to know, Mum already knows I'm living with you, they should guess." Joseph switched the light off, "I must have a word with your Dad." I pulled my pillow down, snuggling up. I was tired and a bit upset. If that was a proposal, it was not the best.

The next morning Joseph left early as he had some errands to do, and I tidied the house and cleaned the animals out. I also thought about what he had said. I knew Dad would be ok, he virtually helped Joseph move in and he and Mum would want us to get married. I had not told Joseph, but I was already a week and a half late with my period. I had gone out and bought a pregnancy testing kit but had delayed testing as I thought I was late due to stress. Yet by the afternoon, I was irritable and I was waiting for Denny to call in. There were two tests in the kit so I thought I'd use one of them and save the other. I read the instructions and held the tip under my urine for a second, and then sat and watched for two minutes thinking the line that was supposed to appear would not.

As I scrutinized the test, I could see a faint line appearing where it had indicated for a positive one. I clutched the test stick so tight I nearly broke it. I started to panic inside, there was no way we were ready for this. I reread the instructions to see if a faint one appeared anyway. However, the feint line was now a clear definite line and I ran down the stairs so excited I did not know what to do. I thought I should tell Joseph when he got home, as I wanted to see the look on his face. I could not wait and rang him at work. "Sorry for ringing but I had to, guess what?" He did not answer me and I continued, "You are going to be a Dad, I just took a pregnancy test and it's positive."

"Really?" I could tell from the excitement, in that one word, he was pleased. "Yes, I couldn't believe it, but it's positive."

"Look darling, I have to go I'll speak to you later," Joseph hung up. I went into the kitchen to put the kettle on. I was so excited, yet scared. The doorbell went and Denny stood there with a big shopping bag. "Come in, kettles boiling," I said, and she followed me through to the kitchen. "Guess what?" I said beaming all over my face.

"Joseph's asked you to marry him," she replied, straight away.

"Well yes, but there's something else," she looked at me gone out, and waited as it was clear she had no idea. "I'm pregnant."

"No," she whispered, and then she grinned, "So is Jane, she's due in June," then she laughed out loud, "How are you going to tell Mum and Dad?"

"Well we were getting married anyway, not that anyone will believe us, this is your fault, you said two years to me, so did Jane, more like two seconds." I looked at her.

"Well I didn't count on Swiss timing," Denny said laughing.

"Ha ha very funny, nor did my GP," I made the tea and passed her a mug. "Joseph will have to ask Dad and then tell him he's going to be a Grandpa again."

"Better make sure Dad's gun's locked up," said Denny. I knew she was joking.

Dad did not have a gun, but it was a good job. "The sooner we say the better," I sat down in the lounge, "What do I do now?" Denny had five children. "You make an appointment with your GP and he will get a midwife registered to you and will work out the rest. When did you have your last period?"

"Not sure but I'm a week and a half late." Denny started to get her diary out and after a few minutes she said, "Right it will be due in September." She finished her tea and after some idle chitchat promised, she would keep the news to herself. As I waved her off, I could not wait for Joseph to get back, but knew I would not see him until morning. I called Jena and Jazz into the lounge and put the television on. I was unsettled as I kept thinking of the baby growing inside of me.

In the morning when I woke up, Joseph was sleeping. I tiptoed downstairs to make a drink. In the back lounge, there was a cardboard box on the floor, and a little kitten appeared from behind the curtain on the windowsill. She was meowing and I picked her up. I was surprised, as Joseph had not mentioned to me that he was getting a kitten I stroked her and was rewarded with an enormous purr. I decided to let the kitten get used to us first and then introduce the dogs. I still had Fiver and Pepper who lived in the conservatory and in the garden. The dogs and they were fine and they slept together.

I had a cup of tea and went back upstairs to get dressed so I could go out into the garden. Joseph was awake when I went up and he called out to me. "Where's the future Mama then?" I entered our bedroom he was still lying down, as I bent down to kiss him, he patted my stomach, "Morning, morning," he said giving me a kiss."

Andrea said to me, "Your life is very unsettled, you hardly knew Joseph, met him by chance. Then you are still unsure of his intentions, hardly having time to get to know each other. I mean you hadn't had chance to live a bit with him had you?"

I shook my head, my life always seemed unpredictable and in the fast lane. I understood what she meant. Joseph and I had not been out together a lot. I had not even spoken to his parents; we had not properly planned anything but just sort of fell into everything.

CHAPTER 10

Wine and Wedding

"After breakfast, we headed for Mum and Dads. I made it easy for Joseph, I said, "Dad, Joseph wants to ask you something in private." Both Mum and Dad looked from one to the other, Mum turned and wiping her hands on her apron said, "I'll put the kettle on." Dad walked through the lounge to his study at the back and Joseph followed and shut the door. Mum came and hugged me, "Is he going to ask him?" I nodded smiling.

"There's something else Mum and believe me, we have been taken by surprise and I was only following the Dr's advice, and Joseph was going to ask Dad ages ago, we discussed it earlier this year." Mum looked at me. "Well what is it?"

"Well you know you have six grandchildren and you are going to have a seventh in June, well you will have an eighth in September." Mum looked at me and she looked surprised, before she could say anything Joseph and Dad came through both were smiling like mad. "Did you tell him?" I asked Joseph, he nodded smiling. Dad looked pleased. "Well Grandpa what do you think of another grandchild?" I laughed and then felt bad as Joseph was shaking his head and trying to get my attention. "What do you mean?" said Dad looking puzzled. I felt like I had jumped in with both feet and Josephs. I rushed to our defence. "I am having a baby in September and before you say anything Dad, all we were doing is following Denny and Jane's advice and the Dr's. He said don't leave it too late as I am mid thirties and we thought it would take a while, both Denny and Jane

129

said two years, well it took Joseph two seconds." I finished looking across at Joseph who had gone bright red. Dad turned to look at Mum. "When do you want to get married?" he asked us, "and where?"

"I can't get married in church as Joseph's divorced and ex catholic. I thought Loughborough registry office, and reception at the conservatory club or Masonic hall." Dad was looking through his diary. "The first possible date where I could book it, is the fourth of May." Joseph looked at me and I said, "Well we're going to South Africa in March, so we will still have April left to finish organising. I love springtime, I am for it, but it is up to Joseph." We all turned to Joseph. "Fine, fine but I will have to check at work," he said. Mum and Dad agreed and we all went to have a drink of tea. I was still not sure how happy Dad was about the baby, but at least we had set things rolling. Joseph's work agreed to him having the time off. He wanted his family over, so wanted to ring them up. I was not sure what his Mum would think of me. Joseph moved in so quickly before we had hardly been going out and now I was having his baby. I hoped she did not think I was out to catch him.

Joseph told me later, his parents were happy for him and they would come Friday 3rd May and stay the week. He had not mentioned a honeymoon, and I could not see how we could go if his parents were here. Joseph later told me that we would have to treat South Africa as the honeymoon. "We are doing everything wrong." I groaned, "First I'm pregnant, then we are having the honeymoon, then the marriage." I shrugged my shoulders; I was disappointed I could not get married in church. Joseph did not seem to be bothered. "I've already done that and it didn't work," was all he could say. Then he said, "Don't expect my parents to help with the costs, they already did it once for me."

"Well bully for them," I snapped feeling really annoyed that he did not seem bothered that my parents would have to pay for everything.

I felt under pressure everything was changing at a quick rate. The Dr could not believe it, but was happy for me and had booked me in for a scan at the hospital. Joseph said he wanted to come with me. Our next step was to tell Susanne and Tom, and we had gone over one night to tell them. They were not married but had been together for a long time. Susanne gasped when I said we were getting married and we wanted Tom as best man and her as bridesmaid. She gasped even more when I told her I was expecting; they were both surprised but were very happy for us. We were leaving for South Africa in a week and a half. We were stopping at a well-known winery and I felt extremely apprehensive.

Tina was again going to look after my animals and it would be her last time as she was moving out the week we returned. I was upset but happy for her. Jane had said, "About time too," and Sandra had been happy for us and her Mum was pleased. Mum and I decided I would wear a cream suit on my wedding day; I was trying to be practical and wanted to be able to use it again. We had both agreed I would not get it until mid April because we were not sure if I would put a lot of weight on with the baby.

We had another snag, which was quite a worrying one, and Joseph did not tell me straight away. When he did, it was like a bombshell. He told me he got divorced in Hawaii and although America accepted his divorce papers, and so did Switzerland, France did not. I had to ask him to repeat it several times and still could not believe it. We sought advice, and were told when we booked the wedding at the registry office; they would want all the relevant papers and would have to send them off. We would have to wait to see if the UK would accept the divorce. I was frantic. We had about 200 guests coming. "What happens if they aren't accepted?" I asked. Joseph said. "Then we won't be able to get married in the UK." He shrugged his shoulders and looked apologetically at me. I scowled at him, "So we don't know until the last minute if we can get married, yet we have to send all the invites out and book the wedding and reception without telling anyone." He nodded. I felt like crying but could not. It felt like one of those horrible comedy sketches except this was real.

I thought it fair to tell Mum and Dad and they too were not happy, but there was not a lot any of us could do except follow the procedure and wait.

The plane trip to South Africa was long; it was about 11 hours with a change at Italy. I hated flying and did not enjoy it. The stop over at Italy was different, the airport was full of Pinocchio's and Joseph explained that Pinocchio originated from Italy.

Once we arrived at Johannesburg airport, we had to catch another plane. I was so tired and could not wait until we got to Stellensboch. Driving up the long dusty sandy path full of potholes to the winery, I was alarmed at all the barbed wire and electric fencing. It was even scarier when the owner explained it was to protect the winery. He also continued to warn us not to drive off track, or through Shanty towns and to keep all doors and windows locked at traffic lights, and if we walked through Stellensboch to hide cameras and to not look like a tourist. He said keep a tight hold on our bags whilst out.

The property had an alarm and the owner and his sons carried guns and routinely patrolled the borders. Not used to this, I felt very insecure and uncomfortable. I was not happy at the difference between the living conditions of the blacks and whites, and was upset at seeing some of the shacks they lived in.

Once we had settled in, we took a walk around; halfway up the hills at the back were two natural ponds where you could swim. However, looking at the number of insects and living creatures in the water put me off. Yet, when Joseph dived in and challenged me, I could not resist and swam amongst the lily pads.

The first evening we sat out watching a beautiful sunset over Table Mountain. We could hear the African children singing in the distance. We ate with the family having mashed potatoes and ostrich meat. Afterwards we cleared up and washed the dishes.

Joseph had a whole list of wineries to visit, and we were to travel near to Cape Town and over to Constantia. I wanted to visit one of the biggest and best bird reserves in the area, and a crocodile farm. We visited Stellensboch, which was a lovely area and walked through a nice botanical garden. Joseph had promised me we would look for an engagement and wedding ring in South Africa.

The week before we came out, I had gone to a clairvoyant party with Sandra and Susanne. It had scared and unnerved me, twice picked out of the audience, each time I had been avoiding eye contact with the speaker. They started to tell me things that had happened and it was so true, I had booked readings afterwards.

One of the clairvoyants had taken a piece of jewellery off me and told me Sandra had bought it me. I had never mentioned Sandra to her. She warned me of driving too fast at roundabouts and to slow down. I had also been told I would return to the first shop whilst looking for my wedding ring, and in three to four years time I would meet a lady in her fifties of fairish complexion, who would have a son named Dylan and would become a good friend and help me. The second clairvoyant told me I had been in a long dark tunnel but was coming out of it.

Now Joseph and I walked into a jewellery shop where they made and designed all the jewellery. I was looking for a single stone in a small but neat setting. I disliked flashy rings and preferred a simple but stylish look. He showed us an eighteen-carat gold ring with a diamond and a simple gold wedding band to match and one for Joseph. I liked it a lot but wanted to look around before deciding. We thanked him and went to look elsewhere. We looked in three or four jewellers. I could not find any that were equal to the first and Joseph was adamant he liked the first shop. We were only here for two and half weeks so we wanted to get the ring before we went back. We returned to the shop and discussed the price. We paid a huge deposit by credit card and agreed to return in two weeks to see if they fitted properly.

We walked hand in hand, and stopped at a small restaurant to have lunch. Tomorrow, Joseph had to start his wine tasting. I enjoyed visiting some of the wine makers Joseph was going to do business with in the future. I liked touring the vineyards and seeing where the wine was made and how it was stored. I had the job of taking some photographs, and Joseph had the job of deciding who was good.

One evening as we were coming home there was a torrential storm and in the glare of our headlights, I could see the road moving. It was like a horror story, I had never seen so many frogs, and I was screaming at Joseph not to run them over. He must have hit some, as there were more frogs than road space. Joseph was laughing and I was screaming every few seconds. He kept telling me to watch my blood pressure.

The next morning he took great delight in telling everyone I had set up a save the frogs campaign, and was going to build a tunnel under the road. We set off for Hermanus having planned to stay overnight. It was on the coast, and I regretted it was the wrong time of the year to watch the whales. I liked Hermanus and we walked along the coast watching the waves crash amongst the rocks.

The next day Joseph took me to a crocodile farm, the first thing I saw was two ostriches, being hosed down, and they loved it. The crocodile farm was interesting, but after half an hour I had enough, I think Joseph had too. He bought a tin of crocodile pate from the farm shop and we headed for the Hamilton estates in Constantia. The vineyard was very pretty with a few lakes for the birds, and I enjoyed sitting out having a break and a drink. I teased Joseph. He sat at the table wearing a short-sleeved shirt and a pair of shorts. He looked casual smart. I loved his muscular body. I had never seen any man with such big muscles and although he was small, he was strong. Mum said he was compact. "When are you going to propose then, we will have the ring soon, you don't know if I am going to say yes?" I raised my eyebrows at him waiting for an answer. He laughed and leant across the table to grab my hand, "I am waiting for you to ask me."

"Very funny," I replied, and we both got up and headed inside.

The time passed quickly, we picked the rings up, and still Joseph would not let me wear mine. They laughed at the winery saying I would find it in my mashed potatoes. We made friends with another lad who was working there called Emmanuel, and from Switzerland; he was on a learning experience break and stopping in the accommodation for the labourers. He invited us over later for a drink.

Joseph and I sat outside on the grass watching the geese. I was a bit scared of them. We were aware of the time, as Emmanuel had said eight and it was quarter to. Joseph disappeared round the corner and came back with a bottle of champagne, two glasses and a single red rose. He filled my glass, "Right you have three choices, Zulu, Swiss, or English."

It was very romantic with my glass of champagne, and my red rose looking at the sunset over Table Mountain, and the children singing again, echoing in the distance. I looked at him, "Zulu of course," I said, he laughed.

"I should have guessed, well we'll have it in Swiss first, and practice the Zulu later." Joseph's Swiss, as he called it was Swiss French, although his Dad knew the Swiss German too.

He took my hand and placed the engagement ring on my finger, and said,

"*Je t'adore avec mon cœur,*" *meaning I love you with my heart, and gave me a loving kiss. I hugged him hard, this was my future husband, and we both clinked our glasses, toasting our future together.*

Joseph took the glasses and champagne and said, "Come on let's share our good news with Emmanuel." I followed him skipping lightly across the yard to the labourers' cottage on the other side. We walked along a narrow path full of rose bushes and came out into a small garden. Emmanuel was standing on a veranda. He came quickly down to greet us. Joseph filled our glasses and asked Emmanuel if he had another glass. Emmanuel went indoors and came back with a tumbler, he shrugged his shoulders laughing; "It will have to do." We all laughed and Joseph poured him a drink, "To South Africa and to my fiancée," he said smiling at me. I showed my ring to Emmanuel. "Wow, that is good," he said. He walked down the steps into the little garden, as we looked out beyond it, the sky had changed to an amazing hue of orange and red, and the black silhouette of Table Mountain was clear. The African children could still be seen dancing in a ring, chanting songs. Joseph was joking to Emmanuel, that I was going to set up a sanctuary for frogs and the evening continued on a high.

The trip to South Africa ended, and we were now busy at home arranging wedding plans. My future in-laws were coming over on the Friday night, Mum and Dad putting his brother up, and we, his Mum and Dad. I was going to sleep the Friday night at Mum's too. Sandra was putting my relations up from Belgium. Benoit, Joseph's friend, who was also playing a part as the best man, was going to take charge of the rings. Tom was going to make the speech. I had Sandra and Susanne as bridesmaids. I had no idea where I was sleeping on our wedding night, as Joseph would not let on. I knew we were all gathering at Mum and Dad's on the Sunday. I was still desperate to hear news whether England accepted Josephs divorce papers."

This was a Friday and Andrea was writing notes as she was away for a week. She told me Dr Lynn would still be seeing me every day. "How did you cope? With South Africa, being pregnant, and not knowing if the wedding would go ahead?"

"Not brill, I was sick on return to England and had to have a scan, but I was still seeing Dr Lynn." I continued to explain.

"I saw Dr Lynn again at the hospital. I still spent most of the session staring blankly, thinking, he was trying to catch me out with many of the questions. He asked about my relationship with my parents, all I could say was, they were the best in the world, and I loved them to bits. He asked about Denny and Jane, again I told him I loved my sisters. When he asked about Richard, I did not say a lot. Just how he helped my parents, and because of him, I managed to get my house.

This was not a great deal of information, and I took to writing what I wanted to say before I went. A pattern emerged where if we did discuss or say a few words I would not talk much but elaborate more on paper. I took sheets of paper in and wrote. Dr Lynn was extremely patient and could tolerate sitting for an hour with perhaps two or three sentences coming from me. Mostly I would nod or give facial expressions.

He knew I was getting married and I was expecting a baby in September. He and a fantastic midwife, a lovely girl called Julie, helped arrange with my GP, that I would have a caesarean birth. He had managed to grasp that I had had a traumatic past but did not know details. I agreed to an epidural. Julie promised she would be with me, she arranged for an anaesthetist who I would meet before and Joseph too would be there. I told Mum and Dad I would be having a caesarean because of my ME. The consultant gynaecologist was a nice man, and he took note that I was to be examined to a minimal as possible. As I was rhesus negative, I had many blood tests during the pregnancy.

The papers about Josephs divorce came the week before the wedding, and the UK accepted them. We were all relieved. I had been shopping with Mum and Susanne, and had bought a simple cream linen suit. The colour scheme for my flowers was peach, so we spent a lot of time looking for a peach top to go under my suit.

Mum and Dad had arranged the reception to be at the nearby Masonic hall, and had seen to the cakes and flowers. On the wedding morning, we would meet at Mum and Dad's, and drive to the registry office following each other, as many people had travelled and did not know the area.

The morning of the wedding, I came out of the hairdressers and went straight home, it was nearly half past ten, the marriage ceremony was at one o'clock, and people were meeting at Mum's from eleven o'clock. Mum and Dad had been over to the hall a few times. They were whispering and excited. Joseph and I had bought presents for Sandra and Susanne, and a lovely bronze cast figure of a spaniel leaping into the air for Mum and Dad, and a photo frame with a vine leaf decorating it for Joseph's parents.

As the registry office asked us to limit guests to thirty, only close family and friends attended the ceremony. We were to meet other guests at the Masonic hall for the reception at two o'clock afterwards. The procession set off at twelve. I was in Dad's car with Mum and Dad, and my aunt. Joseph followed with his family with the rest behind.

Dad drove slowly and it was great to see this enormous crocodile weaving in and out of the traffic on route to Loughborough. Once we arrived at the registry office, we had to wait outside in the car park. There was blossom on the trees and it was a real spring day. The photographer was there and he wasted no time in starting to take some group photographs. We were also having a video. Strict rules allowed no filming inside.

Eventually, everyone just managed to get inside. I stood by Joseph; we squeezed each other's hands for reassurance. Joseph managed to speak his oath emotionally and well. When it was my turn to speak, my voice shook and came out in a squeak, shaking, again I tried to gather myself, and finally the words came tumbling out. We signed the register and Benoit and Sandra, witnessed the signatures.

We rose as man and wife. The sun shone, as we walked through the door into the garden. A shower of confetti rained down, and laughing we kissed each other as the cameras flashed and people came forward to offer their congratulations.

We were late arriving for the reception, everyone crowded round wishing us the best, and lucky black cats and decorated wooden spoons surrounded us. The master of ceremonies asked everyone to go upstairs.

As everyone went up, we grabbed a minute to ourselves and Joseph turned giving me a gentle kiss on my lips, holding my hand leading me slowly to the foot *of the stairs. We heard the master of ceremonies asking everyone to stand up to greet the newly weds and it was our turn to enter. The room looked fantastic and I had a lump in my throat as every table had a little Swiss flag and union jack in a tiny holder on the table. The circular wedding cake in the corner had peach flowers delicately arranged all over it. I walked quickly to our place waiting for the applause to stop before we sat down. I sent Mum a loving gesture of thanks, and I knew she understood what I was thanking her for. Later, I found, she had been up half the night, making the flags.*

The reception went well; Dad had arranged that one of my cousins repeated the speeches in French. This brought about some amusement, especially with the jokes. The party went on well towards evening.

Joseph and I had picked a song for the DJ, we both agreed on Endless Love sang by Lionel Richie and Diana Ross. We happily smooched away listening to the gasps of appreciation from the guests. Dad came to the rescue, joining us with Joseph's Mum. Joseph's Dad asked Mum to dance, gradually the dance floor became full, and we relaxed for the first time as everything had gone really well.

It was after midnight when we said our goodbyes leaving the party still going, and Joseph and I headed away to Joseph's secret destination. As the taxi headed through Oakham, I guessed we were heading for the luxury restaurant/hotel where Joseph worked. When we drove through the gates, Joseph was smiling. The driver helped us with our case, and the staff came out to greet us. Joseph had his leg pulled as we went to the bridal suite. The room was gorgeous and I laughed as the staff had decorated it with toilet rolls and had made an apple pie bed.

Morning came and we awoke to a knock on the door and two young girls brought us breakfast in bed. They both knew Joseph. They were laughing as they went out. We had warm croissants, strawberry jam, a pot of tea and a pot of black aromatic coffee. We did not rush, but did not want to be too late, as we had so many guests stopping over and arriving at Mum and Dads.

The weather was warm and brilliant and more like a day in July than May. Everyone sat outside, different adults played with the children and if people did not get a seat, they sat on the steps of the slabs or the grass. It could not have been better. The atmosphere was jolly, yet relaxed and people felt free to help themselves to food or drink. Joseph and I tried our best to circulate and thank people for coming. I gave Mum and Dad a huge hug and kiss, telling them they were the best. I found it difficult to mix with Joseph's parents due to the language barrier. I did try and so did many of our other guests. Joseph's Dad made us laugh, as it was clear he had a huge sense of humour and loved to tease. Joseph's brother was going back that night.

I had mixed feelings about the week straight after our wedding. It was not every brides dream to spend their honeymoon with their in-laws. Yet I told myself our honeymoon had been South Africa, and the week with Joseph's family was important for both sets of parents to get to know each other better.

We arranged trips to Stratford- upon- Avon and Nottingham, shopping, and we took them to Lincoln and visited the cathedral, an emotional trip for me, as I had some brass Lincolnshire Imps that my Nan had treasured.

We sat outside at the hotel where Joseph had worked, with lovely views of Rutland, eating finely made sandwiches, served with silver cutlery and fine china. After we walked leisurely around the grounds and took some fun photos under the trees with the blossom petals.

The week passed quickly and Joseph's Mum gave Mum a crystal bowl she had bought in Nottingham. We kissed and said goodbye, and Joseph took his parents to the airport. I had not leapt into their arms or done all the mother-in-law jokes, it was early days, and I did not really know them that well.

We had some excitement in the summer, as Joseph was to be the wine consultant for a cooking series on television. His job was to recommend the wine to go with the dishes the chefs had made for the program. The drawback was Joseph had to go and stop in Manchester during the recordings the same time the baby was due. I was panicking a little as I wanted the baby, but I was also scared of the delivery. It had not helped with Jane ringing me, constantly asking what I would do if anything was wrong with the baby. It filled me with negative thoughts and doubt.

Joseph had a list of recording dates. The consultant Mr Spencer was excellent, and he told me that I would have to have the baby a week early. He also gave me the choice of three dates. I chose 20 September as my birthday was on the *twentieth, and Joseph had looked at the dates and decided that he would be able to be there for the caesarean. It was my wish; no one knew when I was going for my operation."*

Andrea said, "Why didn't you want anyone to know?"

"I was too scared and I never want anyone around when I am scared," I replied. Andrea continued, "Come on; tell me about the rest, I want you to leave me with a nice ending before I go on holiday."

I laughed, "I'll do my best." I said.

"I went to see Mum and Dad on September 19th, which was a Thursday night. It was hard not to tell them; I gave them both a big kiss and hug, returning to the house wishing Joseph would arrive back from Manchester. I had packed a small suitcase including baggy nightshirts with buttons down the front. I had a sheep design on one and felt it was appropriate, I felt like a lamb going for the slaughter. Yet the little baby grows and outfits balanced the reality back again.

In the morning I gave the dogs a hug and whispered in Jazz's ear to tell her to behave herself, I stroked Fiver my black cat who was sunning himself in the conservatory and left. Joseph and I did not speak much. We were both very nervous. It was half eight when we got to the hospital, and I was taken to a side room which had been requested by Dr Lynn.

It was nearly ten o'clock when a friendly nurse came in and said, "Are you ready?" I smiled and rose off the bed, shuffling down the corridor, following her into a small side room. My heart beating rapidly as I could see through the double doors into the operating theatre.

It was a while later that our baby daughter Jo Jo lay in a baby trolley with clear sides and an orange hospital blanket over her. I could see the tuft of dark hair sticking up. We had both said goodbye to the anaesthetist and were now left alone with a baby daughter in a little bed besides me. It was an amazing feeling that we had created her and she was ours.

I lay back in my hospital gown too exhausted to change, they had endured difficulties with the anaesthetic and pulling the rest of the placenta out, I had insisted on being awake throughout, and now I was relieved it was over.

Joseph said he would go and ring our parents. He came back ten minutes later, excited, saying that Mum and Dad would call in, in the afternoon, so would Sandra and that his Mum and Dad were very happy.

Later that day, to my dismay Sandra turned up before Mum and Dad arrived, I saw the glances they gave to each other, and I felt sorry for them. Sandra did not stay long. I thanked her for looking after the dogs, later explaining to Mum and Dad that Joseph had to let her know, as she was looking after all the animals, as he was in Manchester most of the time.

I lay back against my pillows tired, I happily watched Mum lift Jo Jo out, as she had started to cry, and sit on the chair at the end of my bed. She asked Dad for a fresh nappy and we watched as she expertly changed her.

After Mum turned to Dad, "Would you like to hold number eight?" Dad laughed. "You bet," he replied, extending his arms. He lifted Jo Jo with ease and Mum instructed him to sit down on the chair. She then tidied up and asked if I wanted another drink, and without waiting for an answer poured me some lemon barley water that she had bought. I was glad to see them but tired and I leant back shattered. Joseph took Jo Jo off Dad and placed her back into her bed. Mum, left a couple of magazines saying, "Well love, we'll make a move, we'll come again tomorrow," leaning over she kissed me and so did Dad. They both gave Joseph a kiss and then looked at Jo Jo and went. Joseph sat down, he looked tired. "Do you want to go?" I asked, as I knew he had to go back up to Manchester to continue the TV recording. "I don't, but I need to change and get some more clothes ready," he looked guilty. "Go, I'll be fine I need to rest, your daughter's fine," he bent down to kiss me and we hugged each other."

Andrea said, "Couldn't he have more time off than that? It's ridiculous."

"He couldn't, the television series were on a tight schedule, and the rooms they were using were next to Coronation Street's recordings and it was all based on tight timing. Yet, he refused to tell them it was a planned birth. They all thought it fantastic he was off the day Jo Jo was born. They celebrated the next day with champagne in the studio." Andrea laughed. I continued to tell her what happened after.

"*The day we took Jo Jo home, we both felt proud. It was still a wonderful feeling to think we had created this live baby. We were both scared as we felt the responsibility of new parenthood and we were both excited. We had a little Moses basket lent to us by Denny's best friend Imogen, placed next to our bed. We placed Jo Jo with her feet touching the bottom to prevent her sliding down, caressing her hair at the same time. Baby monitors placed in the bedroom and lounge. Julie the midwife came out in the afternoon; she weighed Jo Jo, and inspected my wound and my breasts. My breasts were sore and my nipples had started to bleed so much, that it was agony each time Jo Jo tried to breastfeed. Julie told Joseph to buy a certain cream from the chemist and said we would have to monitor the situation. In the morning when Julie came and weighed her, she came over to me, "Sorry I know you've done your best, but she will have to go on to powdered milk and be bottle fed. Choose which brand of baby milk you want, so long as she settles with it, you then have to stick to the same brand. I will check in on you in the morning and check you're doing the bottles right."*

We both thanked her as she left and Joseph got on his coat to go and fetch the bottles. When he had gone I sank back in my chair, part of me was upset, yet I felt relief, as I now knew I would not have to endure the pain of Jo Jo sucking hard at my nipple, and knowing she would get enough to feed. Joseph had bought the bottles and the instructions were clear.

We spoilt our newborn baby with baby grows and toys. We were also lucky, Mum and Dad bought the cot, Joseph's parents, and brother bought the pram and high chair. We bought the playpen and some of our family and friends bought teddies and toys and new baby outfits. After a couple of months we drew back on the spending as nappies and baby milk weren't cheap, and we soon found out that small extras soon added up. Another difficulty was Joseph was not on a very high wage and although the television series helped, he still needed to be earning more. We had already bought a big second hand desk and we slowly changed the back room to an office. Joseph started to build potential contacts from his work and a useful contact was one of the staff, who was leaving to start a new restaurant up north near Manchester, she asked Joseph to supply and build the wine list. She knew he had the expertise and had won the hotel many 'Cellar of the year' awards with his choice of wines. It was an exciting time for us newly weds, with a new baby, and business.

Dr Lynn decided to send a community psychiatric nurse to see me. It was Monday morning, and the doorbell went exactly on time, I opened the door to see a young woman smartly dressed, with a file under her arm. "You must be Bridget," she said, I nodded and invited her in to my lounge. She was an Asian lady, with dark long curly hair and a very pretty face. Jo Jo was asleep in the portable Moses cot. I had been tidying up a little. I offered Mandy the nurse, a cup of tea and she accepted. We chatted casually, Mandy asking how I coped with the baby, and with Joseph who was out a lot trying to drum up new business, and then out at night. I assured her I was coping fine. She asked me if I had heard of a charity called Homestart who gave support to young mothers, and mothers with young families by either group sessions in the local village or town, or they had volunteers who would come out for a couple of hours and give support. I asked how they gave support, and Mandy told me that usually a volunteer would baby sit whilst you got on with your jobs or they would sit and chat, it was up to me how I wanted to use the time. I agreed that it may be a good idea and she said she would contact them for me. I agreed to see someone from Homestart and after meeting a lovely lady from Loughborough, was offered support on a weekly basis.

It was unfortunate that the first volunteer did not work out. I agreed on a different volunteer visiting, and this time the person who came out was brilliant. She was hard of hearing and we worked our way round it. I was happy with her and spent half the time doing my animals, then half chatting to her. She became a good friend and we both enjoyed the time together. Homestart were also happy, as this was more the situation they wished to represent. Mandy kept in touch with Homestart too. She was still concerned that Jo Jo needed to mix, and encouraged me to think about putting Jo Jo in a nursery a couple of times a week.

Christmas arrived and I fell ill with an attack of Meniere's disease and my balance was so bad that I was bed ridden. I could only just turn my head, any slightest movement sent the room spinning. Joseph was concerned, as he had to work through Christmas lunch and would be back late afternoon. Mum and Dad were going to Denny's for Christmas Dinner. They agreed that as I was so ill, they would pick Jo Jo up on the way to Denny's and later that afternoon would call in and see me and bring her back. I felt miserable, it was my baby's first Christmas, and she was whisked away. I was left with a cheese sandwich, plate placed by my pillow, and alone. It was Christmas day, and I was in a dark room unable to lift myself out of bed or reach for a drink. I could not watch the television as any movement made me feel sick.

It was 4pm, when I heard the key click in the door and Joseph came bounding up the stairs. He helped me put on a dressing gown and we walked down the stairs together. He had put the Christmas tree lights on and the room looked lovely. I sat on the settee and he made me a drink.

Every time I moved my head, I felt as if I was going to fall down. The room went round and I felt sick. I rested my head on a cushion and we heard Dad's car pull up. Mum and Dad came in with Jo Jo. They were sad to see me ill, but I could not do a lot about it. Joseph held Jo Jo, and we watched whilst he opened her presents and gave her some baby toys to play with. We all opened our presents then Mum put Jo Jo on my knee and we crouched by the Christmas tree with Joseph as they took our photographs. We put the television on and had a lazy evening. Jo Jo went to sleep in her Moses basket and the dogs and cats were sleeping on their cushions. Mum and Dad went at around ten that night and we were not long to bed after. I had enjoyed the day but had felt really ill and sorry that I could not have had a better day with Jo Jo. I told myself there would be time to play with her and her new toys.

On Boxing Day, Dad was going to see the Tigers play and arranged to drop Mum off, so she helped, as Joseph had to go into work. We talked about plans for the New Year and she told me how things were at Denny's house and what they had done on Christmas Day. I had not been able to converse a lot as concentrating made me dizzy.

Mum and Dad had refused an invitation preferring to sleep through New Years Eve. Sandra was coming up later, and I was cleaning a little, trying not to over do it, and trying to put some food out and arrange the table. Joseph had given me a big kiss and gone. Jo Jo was not an easy baby and cried a lot for *attention. I had spent some long nights trying to get out of the room. She would wake at the slightest noise and would cry so much that if left unattended she would have a tantrum and make herself sick.*

I being a new Mum was stressed and tentative. The dogs were brilliant with her and although I was careful not to leave her on her own with Jazz, was confident to let the dogs in the same room whilst I was there. Jazz was a lovely dog but she was temperamental and could change rapidly. She still shied away if you lifted your hands up quickly. She did get on with the other animals and dogs and had been brilliant with a tiny grey kitten that Joseph brought home one night. He had said it had been around his work and that the fox had nearly had it. We kept her and named her Smoky.

Sandra arrived at seven thirty and tiptoed upstairs to see Jo Jo who was fast asleep. She came down a few minutes later smiling, and said she knew where the phrase sleeping like a baby came from. She saw the New Year in with me and left soon after."

Andrea interrupted me. "Right that's enough I have to go, and I think you have done brilliantly. You have covered such a lot in a short time."

"When are you back?" I asked worriedly. I hated it in hospital without the visits. It made the days a lot longer.

"In a week, don't worry, Dr Lynn will still see you, keep trying to talk about your past, even the easy parts, it will make you used to conversing, and it will gradually become easier for you." Andrea stood up.

"Have a good break," I said.

"You take care." Andrea replied. She signalled for a nurse to come and I sighed as another agency nurse entered the room.

The next day was Saturday and Joseph and the children came, so we spent time in the hospital grounds. Tee Jay brought a ball and Joseph had packed a picnic. We sat under the huge oak trees to the back watching the grey squirrels dart back and forth. I found it difficult to say goodbye to both children. They found it upsetting and Joseph would have to comfort them when we parted. I would go back to my room and concentrate on putting up the drawing Jo Jo would have drawn me. The week soon flew by and Dr Lynn visited every day. He was patient with me and even when I tried to block him from leaving my room in frustration, he never showed anger. He told me to concentrate on my lifeline and to try to work out what to tell Andrea the next time. I thought about this and could not come up with an answer. "Never mind Bridge," he said. "Continue exactly where you left off and I am sure it will come."

During the week, he also introduced me to his Senior Registrar and another consultant. I saw each of them individually and was wary of both of them. The woman consultant was petite and pleasant and I did get on with her. Yet I was questioning every move and motive and although she was nice to me, it scared me even more.

The Senior Registrar was very straight talking and no messing, and he wanted to give me a wider space and fewer restrictions. This was frightening as I did not feel ready, and it made me feel insecure and scared of myself. I looked forward to the day when Andrea was back.

Monday did come round quickly and I continued to tell Andrea about being with Jo Jo and Joseph.

"I carried Jo Jo up to the bedroom after Sandra left, not expecting Joseph in yet. On New Year's Day, I woke up to find him fast asleep next to me. I got up quietly and went downstairs to put the kettle on. I put the news on and was disappointed to hear the usual glum stories of a young off duty Israelian soldier called Friedman shooting at 5 Palestinians because he thought they hated Jews. I somehow always hoped at special times of the year, that the news would coincide with celebrations, yet the real world continued full of love and peace and hate and conflict. I sat back and watched the New Year celebrations in Trafalgar Square; at least some people were having a good time. I reflected on my past New Year's Eves and hoped one day I would be able to see the New Year in with Joseph and my children.

Joseph was late up, I took Jo Jo downstairs so she would not disturb him and we sat and played with her new toys. I still had to be very careful and moved around slowly taking care not to move my head suddenly or watch the television too much. I could move around, but still felt dizzy and sick if I did too much. It was a question of patience and waiting for things to settle. I had cancelled our date with Tom and Susanne as I needed to rest and I wanted Joseph to have a rest. I knew we would see them in the next few weeks anyway.

Mum and Dad had said they would call in later; Joseph actually had the whole day off and was not due to work until the next evening. Our day turned out to be pleasant and we sat, drank, and chatted. The talk was whether John Major would still be elected in May, or whether the Labour party would win and about the problems in Palestine and Israel. In addition, we were arguing whether Bill Clinton was a nice person or not. Mum was asking Dad if she could have a new kitchen and Joseph was doing his best to be diplomatic when both my parents asked him to back their opposing ideas.

The next few months were busy, we were both trying to get the new business afloat. Joseph was supplying and importing wine. Consulting, doing wine tastings and writing up wine lists. I still visited Dr Lynn yet I could not open up, and I had started to write things down, giving him the written sheets of paper. I did not see him that often, relying more on the visits from Mandy. She was very nice and supportive. I still disliked taking Jo Jo out in the pram, preferring to drive anywhere with her in the car.

It was the beginning of May, and just before our first wedding anniversary, the Conservatives lost the general election after 18 years and Tony Blair leader of the Labour Party became the new Prime Minister. It meant change, which was a bit worrying when we were setting up a new business. We continued to do our best and Joseph worked nearly around the clock. We had discussed having another child and although we both knew that I should not leave it too long, we both wanted to make sure we were financially secure. I was keeping myself busy. I had started a distance learning writing course, deciding to try to write a few more articles. I was still not ok having dizzy spells and feeling weak now and again.

The Dr's said it was part of the ME, and that both the ME and Meniere's *were chronic which meant they would reoccur. Dr Lynn never gave me a diagnosis. He was very patient, sitting opposite me in silence for nearly the whole of the session. It was only towards the end of the session that I would be able to utter a few words. I never understood why he wanted to see me. In addition, the questions Dr Lynn asked were difficult and I genuinely had no answer. He would ask a question relating to the past, and before it would engage in my brain, it was as if I had automatic barriers. I would go blank as my mind would not let me recall the question, and because I could not recall or process it, I had no answer. These incidences would occur regularly. They happened daily and numerously for over twenty years. My whole mind would block easily any trigger that was a potential danger. This became a disadvantage as well, because sometimes it would block automatically when I did not want it to. In addition, my safety system became so inbuilt that any trigger slightly indicating danger became so enhanced that I became impulsive.*

My safety system actually became harmful. These processes all processed at a subconscious level, so I had no control whether I would impulsively bolt, or freeze. Whichever decision the process carried out, the consequent behaviour was at a subconscious level, and with no thought to the outcome. In between these states of mind, I was perfectly rational and ok. Another part of my safety mechanism was to analyse thoroughly the reason of any action from the person who was with me. I was so sensitive I would react to minor actions that most people would probably ignore or not count as so important.

Joseph accepted my visits to the hospital, he knew that I had a troublesome past, but did not know the extent and never asked. He always said the past was the past, and we had to move forward. I agreed with him and was eager to throw my past away. Yet I had connections such as my real Mum and Dad that were past, yet still present. In addition, the people or events of my past where I wanted to move on were still part of my present day."

Andrea said, "You seem to reflect on your past and your actions. If you understand how your mind is reacting, do you think about why it's doing it?" I stared at the floor; it was a question where my mind would not go and as much as I wanted to answer her. I could not. I felt dizzy and confused. I just shook my head. Andrea said, "Never mind Bridget, carry on where you left off." I stared at her. I had not realised before, she was writing down comments as I was telling her about my past. She looked up at me. "Don't worry, it's nothing serious, it's just notes for me as I forget sometimes." I continued. "I don't know where to start from, do you want me to tell you about having Tee Jay or tell you from Jo Jo onwards. Not a lot was significant that year." I waited, paused for an answer from Andrea.

"Just continue where you feel comfortable," said Andrea.

"Okay but I have given you details how I felt having Jo Jo, so I will just tell you about when I had Tee Jay."

"It was coming up to the summer of 1998, I had been asked to go into hospital on the night of July 12th to have my second baby, by caesarean on the 13th July. I refused to go, as the football world cup final was that night and I asked to go in early on the same day I was to give birth. Tee Jay was born that morning by caesarean and everything went to plan. I stayed in hospital for a week, and then was discharged. This time Joseph was around a bit more. The wine business started to pick up, and Joseph was very busy working at the restaurant, and building his own business up."

The next week or so I talked to Andrea about how it felt to be part of a family and responsible for two young children. I was not sure, where all this was leading, but the next week both Andrea and Dr Lynn came into my room together. At first I bolted. It was the nurse on duty, who caught hold of me and stopped me from escaping. I sat on the bed shaking whilst Dr Lynn and Andrea both waited for me to calm down. It was a while later that Dr Lynn broke the silence. "We think you have done brilliantly so far and I now want to concentrate on some more of the difficult aspects of your past." he looked at me, paused waiting for a response. I stayed silent. He said, "I know it will probably be too difficult for you to talk, yet writing it down and drawing pictures may help. I want you to talk as well." My heart was beating fast and I was already panicking at the expectations expressed. Dr Lynn spoke calmly, "I want you to try to explain how you met the Bank Manager." I jumped and could not stop myself. I felt shaky and already wanted to start drawing the vivid images that had appeared in my mind.

Dr Lynn and Andrea stood up, "See you tomorrow Bridget, and please think about what we would like you to do." I sat desperately on my bed clinging and squeezing the sheets. I was not concentrating on what I was doing. I concentrated on talking to Joseph and the children at 4pm, and then I tried to work. My memories of the Bank Manager made everything bad, I drew a sharp pointed jagged piece of glass, shading in the tip as if it was blood. As I drew the images of sharp points and patches of black, the feelings did not escape instead they fed on the images. My adrenalin rushed and I suddenly jumped off my bed and rushed straight at the window. I hit it with all my force and smashed through the reinforced glass with my hands. The nurse pulled her alarm tags, and all hell let loose. I did not even feel them pulling me off the glass. Two nurses were holding on to me either side, another two sat at the front and one was guarding the room where I had smashed through the window. I looked down at my hands and arms covered in cuts, and bleeding. Another nurse appeared to patch me up. I sat apologising and wondering what was going to happen next.

I was lucky. I had a very understanding consultant, and the nurses on duty that day were full of empathy and support. I decided that I should try harder and did my best to relate back about my past and the Bank Manager.

"In October, Dad dropped me off and I waited at the doors not knowing anyone, or what, I was supposed to do. I felt strange dressed in a skirt. It felt like a Sunday. I did not have to wait long before a pleasant looking girl came up and introduced herself as Tina. She unlocked the door and I took my first steps into my first job.

I soon realised as any newcomer in a job you are made the scapegoat, and I was making the tea and doing the errands. I made friends quickly and learnt quickly too. Yet my first job was not without problems, the branch staff split into two parties. As I had been accepted into one party, the other took a dislike and because the other had a certain lady member who was a senior and in charge. I was a target of the worse sort of bitchiness I had ever come across.

Although I did not let it get to me, other members in my party, stood up for me and the bank became a battleground of unnecessary unpleasantaries and bitterness. It started to affect my health and I started to have black outs which involved another medical, where the Dr blamed the air conditioning. I was in a vicious circle and knew at that time in my life I must find my real mother. I loved my parents, but felt there was something missing and I wanted more.

Under the new legislation act anyone born before a certain year needed to see a counsellor before they could get access to any information. It was a tricky time for me, as any time I had tried to ask Mum and Dad about my real parents they did not want to know. As far as they were concerned, I was theirs and that was that. I did not want to hurt them but I still had a deep desire to find out who I was and where I had come from. In addition, I was envious of the relationship between my Mum and younger sister Denny.

CHAPTER 12

The Bank Manager

At the bank, the situation was so serious; we were going to be split up. Members of the staff routinely moved due to security matters. It shocked me. Before I knew it, a Manager from a neighbouring branch visited our branch and he came and introduced himself to me. I was good at marketing and he needed extra accounts promoted. He told me I would be moving to his branch shortly. I did just after my 17th birthday.

I learnt which bus to catch to my new branch and as the bank manager had already introduced himself I at least knew one person and the staff made me feel welcome. There was a young girl there, who had been the favourite at selling the accounts, and although she was nice to me on the surface, I was not sure deep down, if she did not resent competition. I genuinely got on with the people and found that the same customers would come back to see me, and if I felt they would benefit from some of their money being put into a new account that would give them a much higher interest, then I would point it out. Most of them were grateful. In this new branch, I met many people and made new friends.

At the bank, I went out with a couple of the lads. It never got serious as although they were nice I was uneasy about having a relationship and it never got further than a kiss. I also wanted to find the right person so much, that although I could have a laugh, many of the men I treated more like a brother. I was competitive and even liked darts matches.

When I knew the lads went to the pub in their lunchtime I soon went with them, and we had a laugh and soon other females came and it was girls against boys. I also spent some of my lunchtime visiting some of my new customers who had invited me for a cup of tea. One old man was lovely and he looked forward to my visits.

I was now just over 17 and had a good figure. I got used to wearing pencil skirts and loved to wear my dark brown slim fitting one, with a bright mustard v- neck top and put really dark brown eye make up on. I looked Spanish with my very dark complexion and although this bugged me, with most of my family being fair, I liked to enhance the tan and look different.

The new Bank Manager was a small man in his forties who had a very strong character and reputation, people didn't mess with him, and although he joked a lot with the female staff, if any of the males stood up to him, he was quickly trodden on and humiliated. He was nice to me and although I knew some people were scared, I did not feel afraid. He reminded me a bit of a cross between Paul Newman and Steve McQueen. He had piercing blue eyes and blonde hair and looked like a schoolboy. He made me feel good if I did the job right, and I soon started to look at this bank as another family.

I did not forget my mission to track my Mum down and asked for an extended dinner hour from work, so I could meet a counsellor in town. The Bank Manager reassured me that if there were any problem to turn to him, and he would help me. I met the counsellor at the town hall square, and gave her details of my adoption. She told me my Mother's real name and my Father's surname, and gave me a bit of paper, which, when I saw it ran shivers along my spine. The writing was nearly identical to mine and the way I wrote y's sometimes loopy sometimes straight was identical.

My mother had written that she wanted her baby to have a better life than she could give. I was in an emotional turmoil. My Dad was a 20 year old who had been working in the Canadian air force and had relinquished any responsibility. He and my Mother lived in Plymouth and she had come to stay in Leicester with relatives whilst she had me.

I came away from the meeting in turmoil, full of excitement, yet full of guilt.

The counsellor said she would find out the address where my Mother stayed thus giving me a lead. She asked if she could meet me in the near future at my place of work. I agreed, thinking I would have to ask the Bank Manager.

Arriving back at the bank, I was still in a turmoil and the Bank Manager asked me to see him in his office. I felt warmth towards him as I could not tell my parents about the meeting, and it was nice to know someone else cared. He told me I could use his office and we made an appointment for the counsellor to come near closing time, as he said after he would help me with the information. The meeting took place a few weeks later. I was buzzing with excitement, as I wanted to know where my Mum had come and stayed to have me.

As I sat at his huge desk staring at the notes the counsellor had brought, part of me was in the room and part of me was staring down again. I was scared, as the search for my Mum depended on the next bit of information I was going to get.

The counsellor was lovely, asking how I was doing, and commenting on how nice it was to have an understanding boss. I could hear the other staff leaving and hoped she would not be too long, as I had not told my parents I was going to be late. I stared at the filing cabinet as she pulled out a piece of paper, part of me wanted to hear, the other did not. She told me an address where my Mother had stayed and the dates at the time, wished me luck shook my hand and prepared to leave. As I saw her off the premises, my mind was racing as I thought I recognised the address. The previous branch where I had worked had many customers living in that area. Still thinking about it, I smiled as the Bank Manager returned from seeing the staff out, and reopened his office door to me. I went and sat down in my previous place and he shut the door behind us, "Well, how did you get on?" he asked. I shuffled through the pieces of paper and passed him the one with the address on it.

"Do you know of this street?" I asked, he took it from me and reading it; he took his glasses off and laughed, "You should know, shouldn't you,"

I grinned looking at him, "It's about 2 streets behind your last branch," he said, as he put the paper back in the folder. He walked from behind his desk, and continued to walk to the filing cabinets placed in a row, in a narrow part of the *office. I stood picking my handbag up, putting the important papers into it. Before I could put on my coat, he walked up to me, and taking my arm led me to the filing cabinets. I turned to look at him puzzled, but before I could say anything, he said, "Are you sure you're ok?" I stared at him feeling an enormous wave of emotions starting to rise. I fought them back, "I'm fine."*

He held my chin up, "Are you sure?" I looked down, not wanting him to see any emotion I had. He suddenly pushed me against the filing cabinets, his lips pushing hard against mine. As I battled to free my mouth, he started pushing my skirt up, breathing heavily, and becoming extremely rough. He kneed me in the stomach, gasping I doubled up with pain, and he took advantage entering me forcefully. I could not move, I could not speak, then I was literally forced off the ground and the pain overtook everything else. It was as if it was in slow motion, banging back and forth against the filing cabinets, and the noise was deafening.

I was in my bedroom, and as I stared at my skirt, I pushed it quickly into the laundry basket; there was blood all over it. I had blood down my legs, and it had marked the bedspread. I went into the bathroom to wash it off. After pulling my jeans on, I went quickly into the kitchen and smiled at Mum and Dad, "Hi, sorry I'm late for my tea." Dad poured me a cup of tea and Mum took my dinner out of the oven, "Had a good day?" they asked.

"Not bad," I replied.

The next day at work, the Bank Manager acted as if nothing had happened. The next few days turned into weeks. Before I knew it, the Bank Manager was asking me into his office to help him. The staff knew when the door was shut, not to disturb him. It was a rule. It was also policy to have two members of staff whilst working in the walk -in safe and Terry the Bank Manager would say, "Come on Bridget, move your queue and come and help." I had no choice. I would close my till, apologise to the next customer, and move to follow him. He would put the two standard keys into the doorway of the safe and turn the wheel like a door hatch on a diving bell, he would pull the heavy door open walking into the safe, waiting for me to enter. It was procedure to pull and lock the door after you, which he would do. I had nowhere to run, and as he advanced on me, my mind took over, and I was unable to react, I would block out the next events and would not be able to recall anything afterwards. I sometimes would not recall driving home after. I never intended to do this and had no control over it. I had a new autopilot that took control and it took control in a big way, as I barely recalled what had gone on, even days later.

This new routine became a way of life and it was as if I had developed a new safety mechanism. Time moved quickly and a couple of years passed. I survived with my new coping mechanism, and I became so used to the Bank Managers demands, that the ruthlessness of his actions did nothing to me. I did not flinch when he took me repeatedly into the bank safe. He would make up jobs to be done like sorting old accounts and refiling securities that were in there. As he was the Manager in charge and signed the appropriate papers, no one questioned the time that we spent in the safe.

He got braver as the time passed and became more confident, he would start to get his Swiss penknife out, and at times would light his lighter. He could not smoke, as the fire alarms would have gone off, yet he took delight in holding the lighter close to my private parts and laughing. He would always do that at the beginning so any smell of burning or singed hair had disappeared. He was always careful to wipe away the bloodstains. My coping mechanisms had gone into full time alert and even to the extent that if he used his knife or lighter, I would not know until later on. I would find marks or would feel pain at odd moments, but it disappeared, and if I concentrated on other things in my life, I managed to block everything out. Sometimes I would lose consciousness and even after the event would collapse, and he would make out I was hot and had fainted. I was not conscious of doing this. I actually started to put all my focus on my bank colleagues, and any minor kind thing they did to me meant so much. I started to value them a lot more than normal. My whole perspective of life was now distorted.

At times, the pain would become so unbearable that I would pass out. Then to my alarm it started to happen when I least knew about it, and I started to have blackouts at work, and the odd one even at a badminton match. Some days I was completely out of control shaking uncontrollably, people thought I was having a fit. I was so out of it I could not explain. I also was unable to talk, move, or explain so it was frightening for all concerned."

Andrea asked, "What did your parents think?"

"They did not know. I managed to keep it from them," I replied.

"I carried on as best as I knew how, mostly denying anything bad was happening. I was on a mission to find my Mum. I went to the big library in Leicester and started to look at the general electoral rolls. I found a name to the address, it was a very common surname, and there were hundreds of that name in the phone book.

Meanwhile home life was becoming unbearable as Jane was causing many problems, and I knew I had to get out. At the same time, Sandra had finished work on her home and was looking for someone to rent the spare bedroom, which overlooked the green and church. As she was talking about it, I suddenly said, "Can I come? I'll pay you board the same amount you were expecting." She looked at me and refused."

Andrea who was catching up on my therapy, turned round and said, "That was one of your biggest mistakes, but you would not have known it at the time." I shrugged, as I still believed and remembered how hard it was at home with Jane. I continued where I had left off.

"No, it's best you are independent and find your own place," at the time I was nearly 19 and I so badly needed to get out from looking after Jane. If I did not rise to her demands, Mum would, and I felt trapped. All I could see was a nice room that would be mine and I would be away from pressures at home. "I really need a place and I will pay and you know me please," Sandra looked at me and told me it would be my decision, and to see what my parents said.

Out of the three of us, I was the home bird, yet I was the one to leave the nest first. Mum and Dad were shocked, but they really could not do a lot to stop me and I moved in with Sandra. As I was round there a lot, it did not make a lot of difference, except I was paying my board to her instead of home. One of the first things I asked permission on was if I could have a kitten, I had wanted to bring Judy, but she was old and Mum was at home. Sandra agreed on one small female kitten and I could not wait to go to the cats' home. I ended up with two males, calling the black runt, Fiver and the eldest tabby Hazel. I was reading Watershipdown at the time.

Although I had left home, I still went round and visited Mum and Dad. I loved them, and missed the garden and dogs.

Time at work was deteriorating. There were a few staff changes. I concentrated on working. Some days the manager took me into the safe and I could not recall what happened, then he asked me to sort out the records that were in the loft. I remember climbing the ladders through the ceiling into the loft where there were accounts and files. Shutting the door after me, he pushed me down on it, straddling me and repeatedly taking me. He started to laugh and boast how he could manage it a second time. He penetrated me fast and forcefully pushing so hard the whole floor was vibrating. I stared at the ceiling trying to prepare myself for the pain in case he would suddenly knee me in the stomach or get the burner out, or his knife.

When I got home which was now at Sandra's I would change as fast as possible to my jeans not choosing a shower, as sometimes I would pass out under it. I would concentrate on trying to think of new business ideas or my writing.

Sandra was now an electrical engineer. We went to a few craft fairs and invested in glass engraving equipment, a dentist's drill with different attachments that could engrave on the glass. As I loved dogs, we had the idea of engraving dogs onto mugs, especially the rarer breeds that you could not find anywhere. We found a wholesale glass supplier and started to engrave mugs. We built a reputation and had orders coming in from as far away as Australia. Although we had new outlets, it was hard work, but it took my mind off things. I liked to play with different cutting techniques and used wheels as well as drill heads to cut deep patterns into the glass."

Andrea raised her eyebrows, "You're too multi skilled, do you know that?"

I laughed shrugging my shoulders.

"It was 4 o'clock and I'd followed him from the bank as usual, I had no choice, as I really believed he'd kill me and make it look like an accident, if I didn't. I *got out of my car into his. Both cars parked in a dead end, next to a roundabout, where the road would eventually open when the estate was built. I was in the front seat of his car. He started fiddling with the buttons on my skirt, tearing some off, I was like a robot, partially aware, yet my safety mechanism had come into action, I flinched once or twice as he had the cigarette lighter on and was laughing. I could see the pattern of the condensed wire rings changing from a bright orange to red, as they got hotter. I could hear him laughing, and smell the burning of my pubic hair, seeing the black hair turning brown stuck on the lighter. I dissociated. I did not remember whether he actually burnt me. I do not even know how I got back.*

I played with the kittens, concentrating on my writing. I also started to try to categorize some of the names the counsellor gave so Sandra could ring them from her work. My goal was to find my Mum.

As time went on the Bank Manager got more and more adventurous, demanding to see me night or day. This time it was late, about half ten at night and he was pushing me on to the damp grass. I knew we were somewhere near a Pool but did not know the vicinity. He had me lying close to a rock, and I was not sure if he was going to crack my skull open. He kept lifting my head up and bringing it down so close to the rock and laughing. I was concentrating on the moon, it was bright, and I could see the map like shapes on it. I stared at the stars, I imagined gods up there, and wondered if there was a god, who might save me. Although I was physically strong, I knew I had no chance against him. I told myself I was strong. I could feel the wet grass and his breathing hot on my cheek, as he panted away. He finished on top of me. The rock came...

Some time later, I came round in his car, and putting my hand to my head; my hair was wet and matted with blood. I felt sick and dazed. I tried to sit up and saw a police car pulling into the car park. I watched as the police got out and walked over to my car. They turned, and I prayed and prayed they would come over and find us. I thought of screaming, he firmly pushed me down; I knew I was unable to move or shout. The police moved away and he let me sit up.

Hazel and Fiver grew into the most loving two cats and they made me laugh so much. One day I locked them in the kitchen and when I was upstairs, I heard a big bang I wondered what it was. They had found out, that if they ran exactly at the same time, and threw themselves at the door, the catch would give and they could get into the lounge. The weight of one cat would not succeed and the timing had to be perfect. It was a nuisance but funny at other times. My little black half-Siamese, Pepper would follow them.

Mum had a cousin who lived in Bolton and she and her husband had a great sense of humour, on the few occasions they had visited whilst I was a child. I would build up confidence to go and sit at their feet, never having the confidence to sit with people preferring to be on the ground and to get as close as I could without imposing. Now I had my car, I invited myself up to Bolton and she and her husband made me so welcome. I went up every weekend I could, and they changed their spare room into my bedroom. I would drive up after work on a Friday and return on the Sunday. The people up there were warm and friendly. Some Sundays I would get upset at returning to Leicester. I was still 19, at the bank and he was doing all sorts of things to me. I did not see any bad, I was deeply fond of Sandra, and she was my rock. It seemed strange but after some of the things he did to me, I would feel safe with her. Yet sometimes it seemed safe to be with him at work. Work became my family, it was stable, and although he did, whatever he did. I was blind to it, I had my friends there and I had some money to pay her board and to keep my cats. I could also spoil my family which I loved doing. I also liked to spoil my Nan and Sandra's parents.

I still saw Susanne every week and we were solid friends. I was coping ok when one day I caught sight of the Bank Managers' wife and she stared at me as she went into his office. I was intrigued as I felt she was targeting me, yet at the same time I wanted to desperately shout to her for help and say, do you know what your husband's doing to me? I could not, my word against a Bank Manager; also, I remembered my parents philosophy of keeping troubles private. My philosophy became a trouble shared is a trouble doubled. I did not dare share anything. I was alive and coping. He had also threatened to get my little sister Denny into trouble, now working at the bank, as I had a good record.

A turn of events came the next week, the Bank Managers' wife turned up again and walked into his office. An hour later, she left. He summoned me into his office and said, "You're being transferred." I nearly fainted and he told me to sit down. My whole world seemed torn apart and I was scared, "Why?" I asked I worked really hard and I couldn't see why. He looked at me and said, "My wife is threatening divorce and wants to name you." I still did not get it, I looked desperately at him, I was hard working, and she had no rights to move me.

That night I looked her telephone number up. Mum and Dad were on holiday and their house was empty. I went round there and I rang her number, " Hi, it's Bridget, I need to talk to you, please come to this address, the situation is not how it seems to you." I put the phone down and waited, she had agreed to come and see me.

It was half seven and the door bell rang, I opened it, I'd no thoughts of her being angry or how difficult it could be, all I wanted to do was to explain the situation, and she came in and sat on the settee. "The situation isn't how it seems," I said again quietly, but with authority. I carried on as she sat back waiting for me to explain. I told her how he had offered the office to me so I could see the counsellor. I explained how important it was that my Mum and Dad should not find out that I was trying to find my real Mum. I told her how my parents loved my younger sister a lot more and why. I told her it was not their fault, they did not think they could have children, and how they were not to be blamed, and they were still fantastic parents.

I ended up that night off loading all the hurt of how I was so inferior to my younger sister, and that I was trying to find my real Mum. She in turn told me her boss knew my Dad and that he was always talking proudly of me, and that they thought the world of me.

She tried to make me feel good. She even got up to make me a coffee, and for the first time in ages I felt relief at having a friend, I tried to tell her how it had been. How I could not escape from her husband, I told her how he had attacked me in the office, how he locked me up, and how he did things to me. I also told her that he knew my Mum and Dad did not want me to find my Mum and he would often threaten to tell them. How he had threatened Denny's career.

As I was telling her, I realised how desperate I was to share it with someone. This had been going on for two years now. She was so sympathetic; she told me *he was getting his own back on her, as she had been unfaithful. I listened to her and felt sorry for her. She then told me that I had to let him continue, not to let him know she knew and to report to her and she would help me. I was so relieved that I had someone to turn to. She gave me a hug and said she had to get back. It was getting near to Christmas and she asked me to meet her in the shopping centre when I had an afternoon off for Christmas shopping.*

I returned to work and time after time, he called me in to help him in the safe. He was a bright man and cunning and had started to ask other staff members in there to help him. Male as well as female, nothing looked out of place. Sometimes when I was serving a customer at the counter he would lean heavily on me as he spoke to the customer. They felt honoured that their Bank Manager was chatting to them. He loved his position and he used his power. He was a womanizer and frequently chatted to female clients, yet he would joke with all customers.

When he was upon me I did not feel, I did not acknowledge. I think that sometimes he was pretty rough and powerful. Sometimes he would call me into the safe and within 5 minutes, we were out again. He used my body, and my mind separated. I looked down. I was not there. After, I concentrated on work. Sometimes I lost and could not recall time. I lost track of events yet I was here, surrounded by my work colleagues who meant a lot to me.

The following week the weather was gorgeous for the time of the year, it was freak, as it was hot in November. He turned to me, "What time is your dinner?" I looked at him and replied, "Half twelve," he laughed and asked if I knew where the park was and to meet him there.

On my break, I walked up the hilly pavements and turned into the green park as instructed. I did not have to look for him, he made his way over. He put his hand firmly on my elbow and led me to a quiet corner where a small rose bed was. He lay down on his jacket and patted the ground. "Don't be silly," I said. He laughed, quickly grabbing me and pulling me down. He was on top of me, quickly pulling up my skirt. I tried to fight but had no chance and then my control went, I saw a woman wheel a pram by and was aware of a lady walking her dog, she was angry and made a comment, cleverly he made it look as if I was in compliance, he laughed at the woman.

At home that night Sandra came to me, before I could speak, she turned angrily to me, "He wants reporting," and continued, "Mum says I should report him to the police." I felt a panic come and she was shouting, "Sam told me, her best friend walks through that park. I had only met Sams' best friend the other week. She recognized you and him," she walked away from me. I caught up with her grabbing her arm. I pulled her round. I should have felt grateful that rescue was coming, yet all I could think of was I would lose the safe environment of working everyday with my colleagues, and all the nice customers I looked forward to chatting to each day. I could picture it coming out, about my real Mum and I could imagine the horror on my parents face. "Please, please don't," I was nearly crying, "I love my job, it's up to me, not you, don't." Sandra looked at me and walked away. I felt bad. I knew she was upset and I was scared it would turn into a nightmare night. It did.

One late afternoon, after he'd kept me behind in his office. I climbed into my car, looking into the mirror to reverse; the word 'slut' appeared written through the condensation. It hit me hard and I wanted to scream and shout and tell the person, how it was. I wanted to be safe and know everything was going to be ok. I wanted to know that I would not be held captive and tortured, and know that my body was never going to suffer pain again.

However, I could not tell my parents I loved them so much, I did not want them to be upset. I could not turn to Sandra, as she was so unpredictable with her moods, and I too loved her as if she was a mother. She looked after me and still made me feel loved. She would listen to me about anything else and she was working so hard to help me find my real Mum. I drove home slowly, feeling that everyone who looked my way had written the message on the back. Once home I curled up with my cats, I was safe with them.

The next week things really went down hill, he held me down in the car pulling out his penknife. He was always showing off about this knife. It was the Swiss one. Today he pulled out the big blade and showed it to me glistening in the sun. It scared me. He had made me wear my button down denim dress, which was tight and clung to your figure, buttons opened from the top or bottom. I looked at the knife, inside me my heart had started to race so fast, that I started to feel dizzy. I tried not to look at him, the knife kept catching the sun sending dazzling flashes across my face. I tried to look into the distance; I felt the knife on my neck and was not sure if it would be a quick slash or a slow long cut, I was waiting, and then from his reactions, knew he had done something. Yet again, my safety mechanism had drilled in and I would feel nothing. I put my hand to my neck there was blood, but I was still alive and wasn't sure what he'd done, I realised he had taken every item of my clothing off and as I lay naked, I could still see partly out of the car."

Andrea had her hand over her mouth and looked shocked. I paused, I felt nothing, I continued, as I was in a hurry to finish.

"A few days' later people were asking why I had a bandage on my sore neck. "I had an accident with one of the cats," I said as I smiled at Fay, "Yes, I know I'm soft, but they're lovely cats." I moved to my till and concentrated on putting all the Queens heads the right way round. I turned and asked for some spare change, and she clucked, looking at me like a mother hen. I liked Fay she was nearly at retirement age; her husband was a manager at another branch. I started to give Fay a lift to her home, which was also near Groby. When he demanded I would be there at a certain time, I could drop her off. Fay thought I was being nice as it was completely out of my way. I always wanted to tell her and ask for help. However, she and her husband was such a lovely couple and looking forward to their retirement. I did not want to put on anybody. In addition, I was really surviving on a thread, not living properly, but existing.

The rides to the dead end of the road were so frequent that, I had even hardened to the fact that every Thursday, as he held me down and stripped me in his car, we had an audience. The first time I was horrified. He was on top of me in the passenger seat which had been lowered to be like a bed and as he was completely in his own little world, he had not realised a huge yellow dustbin lorry had parked opposite. I could see at least three men in there possibly four, and they were enjoying every moment. They were laughing and excited. I tried to sink lower and to look away, but the firm grip of his hands around my wrists were like iron clasps and the rigidness of his body held mine so tight, movement was not there. When he realised they were there, he looked up, and laughed, they reacted to him by clapping. I was dead inside and I had no reaction.

They were to become regular watchers and some weeks as I lay naked, he would boot me in the back, and as I arched forward, they would watch eagerly. I had been stripped of everything, the only thing they did not do was to come and join him. Yet to me they could have been in the car, the shame could not have got bigger, and the agony already overshot. I felt that things could not get lower. Yet one evening he was on top of me in a different street and as I had a period, he just got hold of the tampon, yanking it out, wound down the window and threw it into the gutter. An elderly woman walked by minutes later, pulling an old-fashioned shopping trolley. As she struggled to lift it up the kerb, I could see her reaction as she realised, she was staring at a newly used tampon, in the middle of the gutter. I felt for her, as she walked off nearly running.

December came and I met his wife in Leicester, she was a comfort as I could not wait to tell her what he had done, "Don't worry," she said, "It will be sorted, you are sure, he doesn't know you're seeing me?" I nodded at her and she said she would ring me after Christmas.

I returned home for Christmas at Mums and Dads. I usually loved Christmas and would spend a lot of money on my parents and try to get my sisters what they wanted. Jane was like a little kid, you always had to hide her presents, as she would open them early. As it was today, she was so excited. "Please can't we open more?" Dad laughed turning and throwing her a cracker.

Sandra was spending Christmas with her parents, she rang to wish me a 'Happy Christmas.' Susanne also rang it was a tradition with us that she would ring me on Christmas afternoon. I was the opposite of Jane. I liked to enjoy and hang on to the moment and I spent ages undoing each present and looking to see who it was from and appreciating that they had tried to think what I would like. I had many books on animals, some painting, and drawing equipment. Mum and Dad had bought me a specialist lens for my camera and I had some clothes off Susanne with some little presents. I had bought Mum and Dad a new dinner set and they were thrilled to bits as there was a lot of extras like glasses and egg cups and matching tea cups with teapot etc. I had also bought them, chocolates, perfume, and aftershave.

It was a nice time. My Nan was enjoying herself on the chair in the corner, she still had her party hat on and I passed Denny the camera, as I hugged my Nan and threw a balloon into the air. We were all happy and tired from the excitement. Mum did the usual thing of going through every bit of wrapping paper before putting it into the black bin bags. We always teased her, but knew she was right, as there were many times she had picked up a small gift that had gone astray with the paper.

It was the day after Boxing Day, when I returned to Sandra's with a big bag of my presents. I spent the morning putting my new clothes away and putting the smellies in the bathroom and ate the rest of my chocolates sitting on the settee with a book and the cats. Sandra was busy tidying up. I returned to work for a couple of days before the weekend. The first day I returned, I was called into the office. As the Bank Manager looked at me, I could tell he was uncomfortable and I felt a panic rise. "Sorry I have to tell you this, but from March 1st you will be transferred to Haynes Road branch." I felt as if my world had crumbled and I sat down, to me this was my home and he was telling me to get out. I thought of his wife and our conversations, as I looked at him he continued, "I know you've been seeing my wife; she thought it was so funny to tell me you'd been seeing her." Then he picked up some papers from his desk and asked me to leave. Later on that day, he called me to the safe and again, as I tried to back more and more into the shelves, he came repeatedly at me with so much force, I watched him wipe the blood up off the floor.

That night at Sandra's, I sat and cuddled my cats, it was New Year's eve tomorrow and I was dreading it, of all the days of the year to get upset that was the one for Sandra. Every New Year's Eve she would get suicidal and every time it was a nightmare shouting to her to get off the train track or pulling at her to stop climbing over the motorway bridge. Mostly she would ride to Beacon Hill, climb up the rocks, sit, and stare out to the sky.

New Year's Eve did come and for once Sandra didn't go out, instead she sat watching the television and chain-smoked. I felt miserable and trapped, my *friends had invited me out; but I didn't dare leave Sandra on her own. She would not have come with me and I felt resentful that I was stuck in a smoke filled room missing Mum and Dad. As the time passed and midnight came closer, Sandra went and filled our glasses with wine. I did not feel like celebrating. I hoped the New Year would bring a change for us all. Big Ben chimed and we stood up to clink our glasses at the twelfth stroke, she turned and gave me a kiss on the cheek. I sat back down wondering if the telephone would ring. I thought about Mum and Dad wondering if they were enjoying themselves. I envied Denny she was at a party, lots of music, drink, and laughter.*

As the next few days went by, I could not stop thinking about the move to the other branch. I would lose contact with my friends, the people who kept me going. I knew I had Susanne but I was not able to see her enough. I felt miserable and the more I thought, the more I sank. Then I thought of how his wife had deceived me, I do not know inside, how I had expected it to be resolved, probably that she would tell him to stop and life would carry on as normal. I felt lost and again wished for my real Mum.

The next day it was Saturday and pouring with rain. I was restless and needed to get out of the house. I missed breakfast, got into the car, and drove towards Groby, deciding when I was near to ring the Bank Managers' wife.

I pulled up in a shopping precinct and bought a chocolate bar. Then I came out and started to walk, and for the next few hours just kept walking. I recognised some factories realising I had walked about twenty miles and nothing had changed. I headed back for the pharmacy next to the car. As I walked to the shop I felt desperate and desolate, I could see no way out, losing my energy and morale. I bought a bottle of paracetamol. I was tired. I just wanted to sleep with no disturbance. I walked back to my car and without thinking; I started to swallow the pills. They tasted horrible and I was half vomiting, swallowing them. I had nothing to take the taste away and managed to swallow about a dozen. Then I felt desperate to talk to her to explain again, it was not my fault, I needed to be around my colleagues. I rang their number from a phone box next to the car park, I shivered it was the 5th January and freezing cold. The rain pelted against the glass and then she answered, "Hello who's calling please?"

I tried to speak and was nearly whispering, "It's Bridget, I'm near your house, I've taken some paracetamol and I don't know what to do, I was upset at being transferred." There was a pause and then she came back on to the phone, her voice rushed and exasperated, "How many have you taken?" As I whispered twelve or more, she came back so loud and so certain, "Well that's not enough is it, if you're going to do it you need to do it right, you need to take at least another dozen." I put the phone down, went, and sat back in the car, taking another dozen. I tipped the pills into my hands and determinedly I started pushing them in my mouth making myself swallow. I emptied the bottle sitting back. Then I could not rest, in the movies people just fell asleep, so I decided I would rather go to sleep outside. I got out of the car and started to walk.

I walked through the estate near their home to a field. It was deserted, and I was soaked. I found a sheltered spot, lying down expecting to fall asleep, but the sleep didn't come, I tried shutting my eyes, but my mind was racing, and then I felt silly as if anyone went by, they would wonder what I was doing. I knew I still needed to talk. I walked slowly to their house and rang the doorbell. She opened the door and was friendly and my heart and spirits lifted for a second, and then I panicked for as I walked into the living room, my parents sat there. They looked worried and concerned, before I could speak, the Bank Manager spoke. "We were worried, we phoned your parents to tell them you had taken some pills and that you did it because you are getting transferred." He and his wife stared at me willing for me to go along with it. I did not speak but nodded, my Dad was getting on his coat, and they told me they needed to take me to the hospital."

Andrea asked, "What did you think when you saw your parents?"

"Nothing, shock," I replied.

"As I walked outside, I still thought I have not sorted it. I still need to talk to her. She smiled, and as I hovered, not getting into the car, which Mum and Dad were already in. She said, "Do you want me to come with you?" I nodded and I got into the car expecting her to follow. However, she shut the door quickly, once I was in,

Dad drove away fast. He and Mum did not say much, and I sat in silence, not knowing if I was going to die or live and not caring. They pulled up at the hospital and walked through to the emergency department. Dad went up and whispered to the receptionist, I sat down expecting to be ages as the room was full. I was called through. Mum came with me as Dad waited in the room.

A nurse stood telling me to sit on a trolley in the corridor, and asked me how many pills, how long ago and what had I eaten. They were taking my blood and I had to give a urine sample. Then they came back and Mum was told to wait. Wheeling me into a side room, they placed me on a bed; a male nurse grabbed both my hands, telling me to lie still, he held both my hands above my head. Then the female nurse told me not to struggle because it would hurt more. She explained they needed to pump my stomach out, and needed to feed a tube through my mouth down to my stomach, where they would feed liquid into it and then pump out the bad. A couple of times I tried to move to stop the tube as it was pushed down my throat, I gagged, it was sore I could feel the rough edge going down my throat.

I was unable to move as he held both hands in a tight grip. I could feel the cold liquid tumbling into my stomach, hearing the contents spill out into a bucket. Afterwards, they wheeled me to a ward, placing me in the bed, near to the nurses' desk. Next to me, an elderly woman lay looking terribly ill. I lay there for a bit and then Mum came in, she seemed upset, and I realised I had blood all over the pillow. The nurses assured her that it was normal, as the tube had probably made my throat sore. I kissed Mum, and she said she and Dad would be back in the morning.

I lay and looked down the ward. It had about 16 occupants mostly elderly and I felt the odd one out. I pretended to sleep as the nurses came and monitored my blood pressure. An hour later, there was a panic around the old woman's bed and they started to pull the curtains around her. I could see the shape of people passing the curtain and hear the whispers.

Not long after, my curtain closed, and I heard a trolley wheeled in. Ten minutes later the nurse pulled my curtains open, and I looked across to the old woman's bed. She was there no more.

I tried to sleep, I was scared, yet I could not turn the clock backwards, I didn't want to die now, but had been told paracetamol were very dangerous, the nurse kept telling me I must drink a lot. They kept filling a jug full of squash, encouraging me to drink. Later I needed to go to the toilet; to my dismay, a nurse accompanied me. She apologized, but told me it was routine. The next day they gave me a bath. When I got back into bed I was told I had a heart murmur and they wanted to monitor it on a machine, so I would be in hospital for a while, also they still needed to keep an eye on my waterworks etc from the overdose.

I felt weak and upset. The Bank Manager's wife had been using me and wanted me dead. Mum and Dad came, and Dad told me off for upsetting Mum. He told me the nurses had given her a hard time. It dawned on me that I had not thought things through; I had not considered my parents feelings. My Nan visited me, crying at my bedside. I had only seen my Nan laugh and it tore me inside to see her upset.

I realised that when I had tried to take my life I had not thought about anybody, I had not seen the full implications. I had not seen me dead. I had pictured me getting some sleep away from everyone and having some peace.

I ended up in hospital for a week. The Dr made out my heart murmur was because of what I did, yet another said I had it all the time. I made friends with one of the nurses. She told me that I had to see a psychiatrist before going home, and to say that I regretted what I had done; I did not intend to repeat it. She wrote it down for me and I kept the piece of paper repeating it. The psychiatrist looked like he was on the verge of retiring and I did not really need to worry about remembering it all. He seemed satisfied after a couple of positive sentences and I left the room feeling he was convinced I was fine.

Mum and Dad took me home Thursday evening. Then Dad started telling me off for upsetting the nice Bank Manager. I felt hurt, but Dad did not know the truth, and I could not tell him. I saw my GP and instead of having the fortnight off on the sick, I persuaded him I was fine. I turned up for work the next day and the Bank manager was in shock. He was not expecting me back. The staff thought I had been in hospital because of a heart murmur.

Sandra knew the truth and was shocked. At work, I moved to another branch and although I found it difficult, the people there were also nice, and after time I started to settle. Then Terry started to ring and demand I met him, I tried not to, but then he started to turn up making excuses. I could not avoid him; he would wait by my car. He told me he was transferring to another city, and asked if I would move with him, I refused, and he was offensive. He would not leave it and in the end, I mentioned to my present Bank Manager, that I was having a problem with him pestering me. I did not elaborate more. However, the present one said now it made sense to him why he kept turning up at his branch. He told me to leave it with him. Whatever he said did the trick leaving me in peace."

I had managed to write about the Bank Manager on paper, I also used illustrations. There was no way I could verbalise all of it, but at least I had expressed what had happened. It was not surprising I escaped from hospital the next day. I rang a friend from Jo Jo's playschool. I was walking down a dangerous part of Leicester late at night. I was not sure what to do. She had been good. "Hi," I said, I then went quiet, embarrassed, and not too sure, what she would do. "Hello, you," she said, "What are you doing?"

"I'm in a mess," I admitted quietly. "I've ran away from the hospital."

"Oh no," her voice sounded excited, then, she continued, "Where are you? What are you doing?" now she sounded concerned.

"Stuck, not sure where, it's getting dark and I am now scared," I spoke as I walked quickly past a sort of remote parkland bit. It was true I was frightened, yet my stubbornness would not let me ring the hospital, I did not want to be there, I was not safe at home. I was not safe here. "I am coming to get you," said Rachel, "Where are you heading?"

"I was heading for the station, but can continue to the pub further along," I spoke, feeling tired, yet hopeful. "Look out for me, I'll ring the ward let them know you are ok," said Rachel.

"Please do that, just tell them I need a break, and please don't tell them where I am."

"See you in a bit," she put the phone down. I headed quickly towards the main road and buildings I could see in the distance. I came out near the station, and the tracks drew me. Deep down, I knew I did not really want this. Rachel was waiting outside the pub, she led me through, and we ordered a drink. "You just sound as if you need some time to yourself," said Rachel. I nodded eagerly, "I do, that's what I wanted, I want a rest and some peace and quiet, at the hospital I have someone at arms length all the time, it's not their fault, I know I would run or do something crazy, it sends me crazy in there."

Rachel nodded, "I can see it would, you are too active, look what if I drop you at the motorway motel, ring the ward just say you are fine and you will ring them tomorrow. I'll let Joseph know you just needed a break, I can drop you there, after here, the deal is, you promise me you won't hurt yourself and you promise me you will ring the ward tomorrow." I sat back relieved.

"Come on, I have to get back, let me drop you off on the way."

At the motel, I booked a single room. I gave Susanne's name and address. I felt like a criminal signing her name. Yet I paid the cash, telling myself the receptionist would not mind who I was. I took the key and followed her directions through to the next floor up. Once in the room, I put the kettle on and was hungry. I bit into a chocolate bar, made myself a drink, and retired to bed in bra and pants. It was already after one in the morning.

I lay in bed, not at all relaxed, eventually falling asleep and woken up by a heavy banging on the door. I jumped scared stiff. "Hello, hello, open up immediately, this is the police." I rushed out of the bed panicking. "Open up now." I was trying to get dressed. I just had my jeans on and half my top down when I heard keys in the door. I pulled down my jumper just in time as two police officers walked in. "Bridget, it is Bridget isn't it?" I nodded feeling embarrassed, as the receptionist stood hovering. The police officer turned to her, "Its ok love, we can handle this." She reluctantly moved away. They shut my door and came in, taking in the half cup of tea left, and half-eaten chocolate bar. I blushed. "What are you doing?" asked, the first one, "Why have you run away?"

"I didn't mean to, I never planned this, I'm sorry, I just wanted a break, it's horrible in there, and I needed a break away from everyone. I did get a friend to ring the ward, to say I was ok, I never meant for trouble." I sat on the bed. The two police officers were nice, "We do have to take you back, I'm sorry," the second one, said, who was very tall with glasses.

"I've just paid for the night and got less than an hour." I said.

"I think we'll see what we can do," said the first police officer.

"I'll go and have a word," said the one with glasses winking at me. I felt more relaxed as they were both being nice again and I felt guilty at them having to find me. The second one came back, "All sorted," he said.

"Now, I don't want to handcuff you, but I am supposed to, pretend we are getting married and I am holding your hand," said the first one.

They were both smiling at me. "Don't forget your chocolate bar," said the second one and he passed it to me. I put it into my pocket. "Where's your coat?"

"I haven't got one." I replied.

"Well, we will be quick, the car's just out there, remember I have to hold your hand, I apologise," said the first one, again. "Come on, pretend we are getting married," he clasped my hand and I held tightly back. We walked together down the corridor to the reception. The girl handed the second police officer the money I had paid. "Thanks a lot," they both said in unison. I too smiled and said, "Thanks." I hardly dared look at her, I suddenly felt awful, as I had drank half a cup of tea.

In the car park, I half ran with the police officer to the car. It was noisy from the motorway. They helped me get into the back and then they both got into the front. The second police officer passed me the money back, "Every bit helps," he said.

They could not have been nicer as they took me back to the ward. On the ward, they were sympathetic and just glad I was safe.

I ran again the next day, even though the ward had briefed the level one nurse. I took my first chance and was successful. I headed for the railway station. The only thought on my mind was to get rid of the distress I was feeling and the pain. It was enormous and as in the past, I wanted to be rescued by the black. I took the steps to the platform, two at a time. In these moods, I had dissociated from reality, which included Joseph and the children, I was now escaping from my own fear and was impulsive. I knew part of me needed help, yet I was too scared to return to the ward. Yet I knew if I did not contact them, I could be dead. I rang the ward and to my relief Melanie answered. Again at the most vital time I needed to talk, my body let me down. I held the phone close and tried to speak. It was similar to my wedding vows, I wanted to talk, but no sound would come out. I could hear Melanie talking, "Bridge, Bridge is that you?" The loudspeaker took over, 'Platform 2 train arriving from Peterborough, on the way to...' the voice continued, Melanie was shouting down the phone, "Bridget, if it is you stay there." I wanted to speak, I ran out of the station and down the road. I walked into a pub and suddenly seeing many people ran out again and headed back to the station. Walking over the cobbled stones, I could see three or four police cars. I hesitated as part of me sensed they were for me, yet part of me would not accept that this was reality. I headed down the steps and turned towards the platform. A police officer headed my way; I ducked into the newspaper store and dodged purposely around the bookstalls. I left him in there deciding to cross over to the next platform. I could see another police officer, yet not too near and I disappeared into the cafe through the opposite door.

Having an urge to jump on to the tracks, I rushed out of the cafe and walked to the edge. Looking down I could see the steel rails glistening in the sun. Where there were shadows, parts were still damp. Searching the platform there were two executives further up the platform, both dressed in long black macs, both with a valise case, one held a newspaper and the other was eating.

Where I was standing started to get crowded and I could see over the other side two police officers in their uniforms talking. A railway worker walked up the other side crossing the bridge further up. I was hesitant as my suspicions were telling me he was not a worker. I disappeared back into the café, and the next time I looked, he was back on the opposite platform. The tracks drew me again and I walked up to the edge. My heart was racing. I felt deep down, that this time I would get my release and escape the fear constantly drowning me. I walked away from the crowd and headed further up the platform to where the two executives were now sitting, waiting for the train to arrive. The sign above the platform indicated four minutes. I had four minutes to decide whether to jump or get on the train. I moved as far away from the men as possible and started to walk up the platform to meet the train that would be arriving any minute. My heart was racing so fast I felt dizzy and sick. As I tried to focus, the tracks drew me more and more. I noticed the railway worker had run quickly over the bridge and was heading straight for me. He was running and appeared not to go straight by, at the last second, he stopped before I had time to react, putting his arm out, and grabbing my arm. He had black skin and a nice face. I could not move, as his grip was strong, "Bridget?" he queried. I nodded slumping back. He smiled, "You had us going, and we had a description of pink trousers that's what threw us." I looked down at my blue jeans. I noticed the two police officers coming over. I felt enormously relieved. "Can they walk in front and not with me?" I asked him pleadingly. He nodded and they too smiled. "Promise me you won't try anything," he said. I nodded, but he changed his grip so he was nearer the platform than me. They walked ahead, but close and I was ushered away from the edge.

We had to walk through a huge crowd waiting for the London train and out near the cobbled car park, and through a small door that I had never noticed through a small room, where a man was swearing violently. My companion apologised and led me to a different small room. I stared at the wall full of lots of tiny photographs of different people. Some were labelled paedophile. I shivered and sat at the table. "We won't be long; we have to wait for a police woman to take you back to the hospital." My companion spoke softly but nicely. I smiled looking at his railway clothes and luminous green yellow jacket.

Later when I was back at the hospital, I was so relieved I did not want to leave my room. I just stared at my pictures taking a couple from the wall and hugging them. "I'll beat this thing," I whispered to the photograph of my two children. Dr Lynn and Andrea were so nice, yet firm, reprimanding me for running, but in the nicest way possible. Andrea asked me about my real Mum and told me to try to write about her.

CHAPTER 13

My Real Mum

"Sandra managed to contact my real Nan through the leads I had. I was told, by the counsellor that my real Mum would be contacting me soon. Months later, after dashing to every phone call, Sandra told me to have a holiday.

Denny and I had a good week in Belgium and I thought I was doing ok, yet as I faced returning to England, I felt I could not do it. I thought that my real Mum was never going to contact me. I still had not fully fitted into my new branch, and Sandra remained as suicidal as ever. Also she was really pushing the glass engraving and I was not enjoying the bank. I started to slip again and as I could not share my feelings with anyone. I slipped further and further into a feeling of doom. I had enjoyed the week so much in Belgium with my cousin, his family and with Denny, that there seemed no hope to what I was going back to. Waiting at the top of the stairs, for Denny to come out of the toilet before we left my cousins, I suddenly knew I had to do something drastic. Impulsivity took over and as Denny headed down the steep two flights of steps to the bottom, I waited until she was out of the way and launched myself head first down.

A scream echoed up the stairway, I was at the bottom looking up into the face of my cousin who was telling me to look at him. Then I started vomiting, it went black and I could hear sirens. The ambulance rushed through the streets of Belgium; I could see Denny and my cousin looking worried. I was shaking uncontrollably and thinking it did not matter if my Mum did not get in touch.

I was in a Belgian hospital for four days, during that time I hardly ate, confined to my bed, the day I was allowed to return to my cousins, I was shocked at how weak and sick I felt. Mum came to pick me up and I returned to England. I was not well and wore sunglasses to keep the glare at bay. I saw my GP, who prescribed valium, and was given a six-month sick note due to prolonged headaches. I became very depressed and started to walk everywhere, sometimes miles. Sandra worked all day, so she didn't know what I did, where I went, or anything else I was up to, I hardly knew myself.

I lost touch with reality, I got dressed to go out in t-shirt and trainers. It was wintertime. I felt nothing. I just walked. I walked in the snow, I had chilblains over my feet, and I had wet trainers. I was not bothered. I was like a robot.

I had some friends who I had met from badminton, Gillian and her husband Frank, he too played badminton. I started to call and see Gillian. She would talk to me, making me a cup of tea. She was good to me. I was still not thinking straight and I wandered around any area like a stray dog. I started to go to remote places such as fields and take shelter under hedgerows. I stayed out all night oblivious to the weather. All I made sure was that wherever I dossed down, I was out of sight from the public.

The odd time I stopped on rough ground opposite Gillian's, one Sunday morning she called me over and gave me a hot drink. I assured her I was fine and I moved on. If I stopped out, I made sure Sandra was unaware. She was away a bit and I lost focus on things. It was one night when I was extremely bad that I left the house and Sandra became concerned. I was not eating correctly, still on the valium and spaced out.

This particular night I walked miles and was surprised when a blue car pulled up next to me. It was after midnight and I was wary. When the passenger door opened, my legs would not run, even though my mind was telling them to. I looked at the driver, relieved to see it was Frank. He was still in his police uniform. "Hi, Bridget, Sandra was worried she rang the police station, I was on duty so said I would have a scout around. Come on get in," he smiled. I was so relieved, I jumped in, and then as he put his arm round me to comfort me, I broke down. The tears were flooding down my face and as I snuggled up to him and started to feel the warmth of his body heat, he hugged me harder.

I was so near to collapsing through exhaustion, I just leant against him, tasting salt on my lips from my tears. I became aware that he was fingering and squeezing my nipples and that the whole of his hand was roaming freely under my top. I was past caring.

After a while, he stopped and drove me to his house. Sandra and Gillian were there. I stepped from the car meaning to get into Sandra's and collapsed on the pavement. The three of them lifted me into Sandra's car and she drove me home. I managed to walk up the stairs and get into my own bed. I slept soundly.

The next few days were hazy I wandered about the house feeling lost. I tried to get into the mood for Christmas. It was one afternoon, when Sandra was at work, that the doorbell went and I answered it, Frank was standing there. I made him a cup of coffee and he sat down next to me on the settee, whilst I drank my tea. He told me how concerned he and Gillian were and that they really thought a lot of me. Before I could answer, he was giving me a big hug and then it progressed from a hug to a kiss on the lips. At the same time, his hand had gone under my jumper. I could feel my breasts being squeezed. Frank was now moving his hands a lot quicker around my body and I pulled away and stood up. I took the cups into the kitchen and when I went into the lounge, he told me he had to go. I opened the door and he kissed me on the cheek as he left. Initially shocked, I then jumped into action as if it had not happened and started to tidy the house.

Thursday morning Mum called in from the hairdressers. I made us a cup of coffee and we sat in the lounge. Sandra's house was a terraced cottage and the lounge was in the centre, off from it was a long gallery kitchen leading out to a small yard, converted into a very pretty cottage garden. In the summer, enormous hollyhocks swayed against the walls, with bright orange nasturtiums creeping out on the bottom. At the back were beans and tomato plants. When it was dustbin day, the passage door separating our house from next door was left open; people would look down and admire the garden.

Across the lounge, past the fire was a door leading to a narrow steep staircase, which turned as you went up to the first bedroom on the right and opposite that was the bathroom. The telephone hung on the wall near the lounge door, placed so you could sit on the stairs and chat conveniently.

I was just offering Mum a biscuit when the telephone rang. I rushed to answer, leaving the door open. I could see Mum eating her biscuit. A woman's voice asked if there was a Bridget there, immediately my heart was beating like mad and I tried to shut the door to achieve some privacy. It did not work, as it swung open again. I hesitated but answered "Speaking," this young woman then went on to make excuses after excuses saying she didn't know how to tell me that even now she had thrown letter after letter into the bin and that she was my mother.

I felt ill; all I could think of was to protect my Mum sitting there. I could not believe this was happening. Mum hardly ever came round, I had been waiting years for this phone call, and now I was in an impossible situation of not being able to talk. My real Mum was asking me question after question and I felt so guilty looking at my Mum sitting on the settee that I answered shortly, and was in desperation to get off the phone. It ended with her saying she would ring again and I hung up.

As I came down the bottom stair into the lounge, Mum turned round and said, "Oh who was that?" I was a useless liar and muttered, "Oh no one in particular."

Yet again, she asked, "Who?"

I had always tried to be as honest as I could, and as she asked, I could feel my face going red, and bursting inside I said, "Look Mum I love you, you know that, but that was my real Mum and I've never spoken to her before and I didn't know she was going to ring." Mum's face dropped and I felt shallow, I continued rushing it out, "I tried to find her and it looks like it has happened. I found her Mum a year ago and she has kept this information to herself and only just let her know I have been trying to find her, oh Mum I love you but I needed to know." I flung myself at Mum, wanting to give her a big hug.

She hugged me back but still looked puzzled, "Well," she said, "Is there anything else about her, have you a picture or anything?"

"No, I didn't know she was going to ring."

Mum then started on that she had some shopping to do and finished her coffee and Dad would be back for his lunch. She kissed me goodbye and left. I rushed to the phone to do a dial back, but before I could reach it, the telephone rang and it was Jimmy from Bolton. He often rang me and I chatted to him not mentioning my real Mum. It felt unreal.

I was cleaning my bedroom and rearranging the animal books when the telephone went. It was mid afternoon and Sandra was at work. My hair was short, I had gone from a size 12 to a good size 14 and on the wrong side of the 10 stone mark. I leapt down the stairs and sort of slid to a halt with my bum on the bottom step, telephone receiver in my hand, "Hi," I said. It was my real Mum, I felt elation and as if someone had passed me a lifeline. She was saying…"I am in the area and can be with you within 10 minutes is that ok?" I heard myself agreeing, and then put the phone down. I panicked; the lounge was a mess with unwashed mugs in the kitchen. I had meant to have a bath and wash my hair. 10 minutes was nothing.

I ran into the kitchen scaring the cats and making them jump. I grabbed the two mugs and washed them under the tap. I then took the stairs two at a time to look at myself in the mirror. It made me feel worse. I was just going to brush my hair, when there was a knock at the door. I leapt down the stairs and went to open it. It would not open, the wood had swelled with the damp, and it was stuck. I yanked it hearing a voice saying, "Hello."

I shouted back, "The door is stuck, can you push it?" Suddenly it rushed towards me and my real Mum nearly fell over into the house. As I looked at her I was so shocked, I had expected to see someone like my Mum. My Mum was as I pictured all Mums, cuddly, a bit overweight, in her 50's and a Mum.

This person did not look like a Mum she looked like a model in her 30's. She was extremely beautiful wearing a smart suit. I was wearing scruffy jeans, a big sloppy Jumper, and stripy socks, which up until then I had not been conscious of in a big way. She walked through to the lounge. We looked at each other, I was very conscious of her beautiful eyes; they were an extremely different colour between hazel and green. She gave me a hug and I hugged her back. I asked what drink she would like and after she had sat down, I went and put the kettle on.

I kept staring at her as I was waiting for the kettle to boil. She was petite, with long brunette hair, probably a size 12 and a very attractive figure. I had a cocktail of feelings. I knew deep down I loved her, yet in reality, she was a stranger.

I wanted to love her as I loved my Mum, but it was a completely different feeling. I felt bonded to her through invisible ropes, yet I could not expand on any feelings either way. The kettle boiled and I made her a black coffee with no sugar as requested, and I had a strong white tea with two sugars. I sat next to her and it was obvious that she was struggling with her feelings as much as I was. She asked me many superficial questions; which shampoo I used, did I take salt in my diet, try to avoid sugar and did I do any weight training?

She told me that she had been a former Miss Plymouth, so had both her daughters, they all did body building and she'd married someone from this area called Dan, who had also won several titles as a body building champion. This all rather washed over me, I had been told I was very attractive having a dark complexion and dark hair and eyes. Yet I was more at home in a T-shirt and Jeans, and a dress would have been out of the question. Although a customer at the bank, who was a photographer had asked me to model for him and I had refused politely.

As she talked to me, her Cornish accent was very apparent. We both tried hard to be polite, then suddenly she put her mug down and we were giving each other a huge hug, tears glistening in her eyes. Then she was telling me that Dan would be picking her up soon. She also commented that he did not want anything to do with me, but he did not blame me. She had met him whilst coming up to her Aunts to have me secretly, so relations back down south would not know anything of it. I realised that I had all sorts of questions, but I was still in shock, as only a couple of hours ago, I had thought she was in Plymouth not ten minutes away. She explained to me that they had come up to see Dan's relations and her Aunt, her Mum's sister.

She liked my cats, and it turned out she had an Old English sheepdog and a cat. She was just talking about animals, when there was a knock at the door. I went to answer it and hoped the door would not stick again. It did open and a young man stood there with fair hair. He looked a bit shocked at seeing me and I invited him in. He started telling me he had nothing against me.

My real Mum introduced him as Dan and he gave me a kiss on the cheek. I asked him if he wanted a drink, and he too had a black coffee with no sugar. He *tried to make polite conversation, it was all about health, and he advised me like my Mum to keep off salt and sugar and told me the best health products around. He looked very fit and sporty. He told me where his sister lived, asking me if I knew that region. I had heard of it as my Dad, had relations around that area, so I made polite conversation back. He was surprised at how strong a resemblance I had to my real Mum. We both were quite petite and had dark complexions and high cheekbones. All the time they were there, I was thinking of Mum and Dad, and I felt a surge of guilt, as I felt I was betraying them.*

My real Mum got up to leave and Dan stood with her, he gave me a peck on the cheek and again told me he didn't blame me, she came and gave me a big hug, saying keep in touch. At the door, he gave me a keyring, an advertisement for the company he worked for, I said, "Goodbye," waving. I put the kettle on and made myself a cup of tea, as I poured in the milk and sugar I thought of their words avoid sugar, I didn't care I needed my strength at that moment.

I sat on the settee and both cats jumped onto my knee. Hazel was a big tabby now and he grunted and purred like a teddy bear. Fiver had turned out to be a real softy and sat closest to me. I could not wait for Sandra to get home. When I told her, she found it hard to believe. The big question was should I tell Mum and Dad?"

Andrea was listening and reading my notes, "This is very emotional content," she said. I shrugged my shoulders and could not comment. The most emotion caused to me, was the pain I went through of finding my Mum. Andrea asked what happened after.

"I received a letter the following week and my Mum sent a photo of herself and one of her Mum and Dad. Her Dad looked like a small grey haired man, sat in a wheelchair. As I stared at him, my emotions rose, he had forced my Mum to give me away. I felt no malice and tried to understand his reasoning. In addition, there was a small one of my Mum and Dan both in tracksuits. There was an address at the top and a telephone number, and for the first time I had real contact. I sent a full letter back and some photos of me and the cats. I felt it was wrong to send any of my family.

I decided to tell my Mum and Dad about my real Mum and although I dreaded it, went round to speak to them. I tried my hardest to tell them that no one would ever take their place and that they would always be my Mum and Dad. Dad asked to see the photo of my real Mum then told me he never wanted to see it again. My Mum looked and would not say anything. I put the photograph away and knew that if I did keep in touch with my real Mum, I would have to keep it to myself. My Dad went back out into the garden and I tried to keep a conversation going with Mum. She did talk and it was as if I had never brought the subject up.

When I returned home, I felt relieved I had told them, but felt awful and not proud of myself. I was also worried of upsetting my Nan who I was extremely close to. She was my Mum's mum and had the most fantastic sense of humour. She was also very gutsy and independent. I tried my best to look after her in her latter years and Sandra and her family were very close to her. My Nan called me her guardian angel and I did my best."

I swallowed hard and turned to Andrea. "I had a really difficult decision to make and I am never sure if I got it correct."

Andrea smiled, "I am sure you did what you thought was best whatever."

I turned to her and described what happened.

"My Nan had a stroke and was critical in hospital. I had decided to go and visit her, when I received a phone call from my real Mum's mum, it was a big shock. I had not seen her before. She told me she was coming up to Leicester to visit her sister-in-law. This was the person who had put my Mum up when she came to Leicester all those years back to have me. My biological Nan continued, she wanted to see me, would I visit her the next evening at her sister-in-laws house, the address was near Wigston in Leicestershire.

I was already visiting my Nan in hospital but knew that after, I could continue across the town to this address, so I agreed. My mind was in a mixed turmoil, I was in the situation of visiting my very loved Nan who was critical in hospital, and then on the same night going on to meet my real Nan who I had never met before. My emotions were travelling around and I felt guilty, especially when I saw Nan in hospital. Although weak and in pain, she smiled at me as I walked to her bed and I kissed her and held her hand. I felt so bad inside, feeling like I was betraying her. I spent all the time allowed with her and gave her a hug before leaving the hospital. My principles and morals questioned to the hilt. Yet I had a deep inner need to meet my biological Nan.

I raced across the town and pulled up in a street with the directions given. I purposely pulled up a few doors down and took a breather surveying the house. I drove on, did a 3 point turn and parked outside the house. As I was getting out of the car, two elderly ladies opened the door and walked down the path towards me. I felt very odd and inside hoped that if there was a god I was doing the right thing and that my Nan in hospital would have understood.

My present feelings put aside, as the two ladies came upon me, each giving me a big hug. "I would not need an introduction I can tell you are Viv's daughter," one of them said. I guessed she was my Nan as she sounded the same as on the phone and had a strong accent. Following her into a small lounge, I was beckoned to sit down. Plates of biscuits were neatly arranged and the other lady named Doris went to put the kettle on. Before I could say anything, my Nan was pouring her heart out, "I have always counted you as one of my grandchildren. I have never forgotten your birthday. The decision to give you away was not Viv's or mine, her Father told her it was the baby or him. He was a navy captain and very strict. It was unheard of to have a baby like that. We thought you would have a better life."

She was very upset and I tried my hardest to tell her it was ok. I was telling her that I did not blame anyone, which was the truth. It was circumstantial and I tried my hardest to lift the weight off her shoulders, which came across so heavy. She gave me a hug and it was strange I hugged her and knew deep down I loved her, yet in another way, she was a complete stranger. In addition, my Nan in hospital had my love always. Doris brought the tea in, we sat, and I enjoyed listening to my Nan. She was a lady of character and strength, and had an amazing sense of humour. I learnt that a huge factory had bought all the houses in her street and she refused to go. She had just been in the southern news. She also showed me a piece of the news with a picture of her in the local newspaper. I realized then that we were very similar and it was probably where I inherited my stubborn streaks. She told me she had been in that house for a long time.

As she talked, I realized I liked her and the way she laughed, she made me laugh too. I was also proud of her and felt empathy that she had the burden of giving away a grandchild on her shoulders. I learnt that she had to nurse my grandfather, and that he and his brothers all belonged and had high positions in the navy. I felt through the short meeting we had, that she had suffered a tough life looking after him. Doris was sweet and both ladies were so delighted when I gave them the vases that I had hand engraved. I found it quite tough to say goodbye and both she and I had tears in our eyes, though neither of us would have admitted it, we gave each other a hug and I watched them in my mirror, waving as I drove off.

After that meeting, my Nan wrote regularly and I wrote back. She also sent a cheque for £500 for me, which I refused to have. I wrote back saying I had my own Nan and had been given all the things that she had thought I missed. It turned into a battlefield and she insisted that it was only money that her other grandchildren had received and that also when she died, she did not want to make it public, for Viv's sake about me, so it would be easier and nicer for her if I accepted the money. I did, as she made it clear it was her wishes. I thanked her. I wrote a lot, she wrote to me too, and we had a very strong bond. She would telephone also.

I kept this from Mum and Dad as I thought that they were so upset after me telling them about my Mum.

One of the other hardest things I had to do was when my biological Nan rang me and asked me to do her a favour. She asked me to represent her and my real Mum's family at the funeral of her sister in Leicester, but not to tell anyone who I was, but to tell them whom I was representing. I was working for Richard and he came with me. Unfortunately, there were few people attending, and we laid some flowers and sat at the back of the service. The closest relatives came up to me after and asked who I was. I said I represented Viv and they said, "Oh you must be her daughter Ann or Dawn from Plymouth."

I replied, "No, I am Bridget from Leicester," smiled and walked away. Richard followed."

Andrea said, "You were put in an impossible situation."

"I always seem to be," I replied. Andrea turned round from the window, which she was staring out, "Start believing in yourself Bridget, you are worth a lot more than you think you are."

I took a deep breath, "I am fine. My Dad always said, he trusted me completely and would never doubt my integrity." My voice shook as I had just lost my Dad the year before and I missed him deeply. "My Nan called me her guardian angel. My Mum calls me a brick. My kids love me and Joseph adores me, I am fine." Andrea shook her head, "Don't play with me Bridget; you need to tell yourself that." I looked at her and blushed.

"Dr Lynn will be in to see you later and I will see you tomorrow." Andrea left and I felt alone. I told the nurse I wanted a drink and she too was glad to go into the kitchen with me to make one. On the way, one of the lads shouted to me and I took a drink to him returning to my room. Later that afternoon, after I had spoken to Joseph and the children I lay on my bed and thought back. The level one nurse with me watched the television, and although I stared at the screen, I was miles away thinking of the day when Dr Lynn saw me in out patients and I caught him out.

I visited Dr Lynn who I had not seen for a long while. I had fallen into the habit of writing to him a lot. Although he was in the background, it was comforting to know that some of the issues with my past were recognised as important to me, through someone else. I could not talk about my past, he would ask questions, and I would answer with facial expressions. He would help by confirming what I tried to express without me talking. He had talked about Richard and when he made out it was wrong for him to have acted as he did, I had actually blurted out, "It's nothing compared to the Bank Manager," then I had been unable to comment and it would take more weeks and hours of silence for him to retract any more information. I would write some events of my past in a kind of short note form. It did not flow and it was like extremely minute information coming out in the odd word filled in with dashes, as I could not write the significant words down. I would put in key letters but would leave spaces or lines so you could guess at the word but it was not there. I liked Dr Lynn and never missed an appointment, part of me wanted to go, as I knew deep down I needed some help. I wanted some recognition of the way I had lived my life, yet part of me was terrified, as I was never sure if he would trigger a memory or feeling that made me feel bad. I never meant to be difficult yet the building was scary. It was dark and gloomy with big sealed windows and tiny air gaps. It took me nearly the whole of the session before I could talk and I was so on edge, if he made a sudden move it would take me all my time not to bolt from the room. He was a tall gentle giant with dark brown hair brushed back receding slightly, a dark moustache that attracted me. Joseph too had a moustache, and Dr Lynn had dark brown velvety eyes that seemed soft, yet when I was scared, I would search his eyes for a give away clue of his intentions and sometimes he would hold my gaze, many times he would look away. He was extremely arrogant and I was never sure if it was because of the way he presented himself, as he was tall and strode across the corridor, or whether he was conscious of being a consultant who held a lot of power. His arrogance counter balanced with his kindness and professionalism, and although I was wary of the power he had, I was glad he was my consultant.

Today I was just leaving the room when he said softly, "That Bank Manager didn't do the damage, it was the person before him, he must have been very important to you."

I answered unintentionally, "It wasn't a he, it was a she," as I murmured it, my legs gave way and I actually slumped against the wall near the doorway. He rose quickly, "Come and take a seat," he guided me gently by my arm and I sat down. "Did I hear you correctly; you said it was a she?" I could not answer or talk. I felt so weak; I just nodded my head slowly. I felt fragile and he sensed it. He changed the subject asking what I was going to do later on, asking me how Joseph was. It was five minutes later when I left the room feeling completely exhausted.

I never chatted to Joseph about my hospital sessions, we were always so busy, he needed time to tell me about the business, and I kept him up to date about the children. It was as if both of us had accepted that the hospital visits were unimportant once I was home. It was far from reality, the visits had a huge effect on me and I would write more and more on paper and eventually I wrote about what had happened with Sandra.

I sat up on my bed. My heart already beating twice as fast, I knew deep down, to get well I needed to take some more layers off, to get to the centre. Dr Lynn and Andrea had been so patient. I reached for my pen and paper. I had written small insights and patchy details before. Yet Dr Lynn knew and I did that there was a lot more deep down to emerge. I had been in hospital for nearly eight months and knew I needed to try again. I started to scrawl.

Mum was talking to my Dad, "I've told the girls to call in for a cup of tea next week in their lunch hour." A rustle of the paper gave a hint that Dad had acknowledged this statement; he still had his head buried in the back pages of the sports section. I was later to find out that Mum meant a couple of girls from her work.

The following week I was practicing wheelies on my bike, wishing I had a chopper like the rest of my friends, when the dogs started to bark. Two unknown faces appeared over the gate and grinning they shouted, "Hello," and started to walk up the drive. The first one was a large tall girl, when she smiled it nearly split her face in two. Her long dark hair shone, she was puffing away on a cigarette. The other was slightly smaller with shorter hair and she too grinned, I could smell the ciggys as they passed me and headed for the kitchen. I was curious but I was also extremely shy, so although I longed to pedal round and have a nose. I thought better of it, and stayed outside doing my wheelies. I had only done my second one, when the gate opened and Sharon appeared. Sharon was my school mate and although her parents were not that well off the kids didn't go without, and consequently she rode up on her bright orange chopper bike doing a fantastic wheelie. I cycled round to the kitchen, this time I had no choice, and I stuck my head round the door. They were sitting at the table laughing and joking with Mum, I nearly wished I could have stopped. "Hi Bridget," Mum said, "Meet Sandra and Anne."

I muttered, "Hello and Goodbye," and gave Mum a kiss before going back to school for the afternoon.

That night I was cosy lying in the corner of the settee watching the television. Mum sat on her chair with a book in hand; Dad was at the Conservative Club. Denny was playing with her friend, and Jane was out as usual. I was waiting for 'It's a Knockout' to come on which was a fun game where adults played these silly physical games and ran round like children. Cleo was on her chair, Anna was at Mum's feet and I was stroking Judy. I would have loved her on my knee, but rules were rules and she was on the floor.

Mum put her book down turning to me, "Oh by the way, I was talking to Sandra, she's my boss at work, and I told her, you didn't go out much and she's offered to take you out for the day."

I sat up quickly, making Judy jump, "When?"

"Well tomorrow actually, I said you'd be ready for ten," Mum looked at me. My first reaction was no way, and then I thought about the two girls, they had looked friendly enough and it would be different, "Ok Mum, come on look, 'It's a Knockout's' starting."

CHAPTER 14

First Meeting

On Saturday morning, I was up early. Mum said Sandra was coming at ten, and from half past nine, I was looking out of the window every five minutes. Sandra arrived dead on ten, she gave me a big grin again and I warmed to her. Whilst she and Mum chatted over coffee, I ran across the garden to say bye to Dad, who was digging behind the apple tree, watched by a robin pecking at the newly revealed worms. "Bye Dad," I gave him a kiss. "Have a good time," he said stretching his back and clapping his hands together to get the soil off his gloves. I ran across the lawn up the steps to the paving area, where Sandra and Mum were now waiting. Mum walked with us down the drive to Sandra's car. It was a white Volvo with bright red leather seats. I slipped into the front passenger seat feeling a sense of importance at the chance of going out with my Mum's boss.

As we turned the corner and Mum disappeared from sight, Sandra turned to me, "Do you mind if we call in on a friend? She's just moved and I have a few boxes for her." I shook my head; it turned out the friend was a teacher from my school. Sandra drove to the neighbouring village, which consisted of a huge estate of similar houses. Every road and house looked the same except for the coloured doors. We walked up the path to a bright red door, opened by a thin looking woman with glasses who ushered us in and introduced herself as Gail. I was disappointed, as I did not recognise her. She was pleasant and took us through to a room where once all the boxes and cases had disappeared, could be a lounge.

Her husband arrived a few minutes later and was pleased to see Sandra. She and I unloaded some boxes from the boot of the Volvo and carried them in. After a while, Sandra came over to me, "Let's go, and grab some lunch."

She parked in a gateway opposite the fish and chip shop. I waited in the car having decided on two sausages in batter with a bag of chips oozing of salt and vinegar. Sandra returned and I could smell the chips, feeling piping hot I had to keep dropping them so they would not burn my fingers, biting into the battered sausages; the oil ran out, they tasted great.

Sitting in her Volvo enjoying an unexpected treat I started to feel better. Sandra sat eating a big piece of fish. She kept questioning me about my life. I fondled the large crucifix around my neck, a present from my grandparents and although my Nan was still alive, it had great sentimental value. Susanne's Mum believed in ghosts and after hearing some weird tales, I hoped it would protect me from the unknown.

Sandra asked me questions that no one else seemed to be interested in, they were quite personal. It started with my favourite subjects at school, to my best friends. I told her how much I loved my Nan and how I hated school. I poured out the problems about my best friend, never being allowed out, to how many cuddles I gave my dog in a day. Sandra spoke too and told me she was moving to another flat, and asked me if I wanted to go there with her.

We finished the meal and arriving at her new flat, I helped carry some of her possessions in.Whilst we were there, her Dad turned up. He was very practical and spent all the time helping put the bed up and laying the carpet down and although he smiled at me, he did not say a lot.

When I arrived home that Saturday evening, I was buzzing and my parents were pleased that their quiet number two daughter had enjoyed herself so much and actually ventured out. In reality I felt a self importance that I hadn't felt before, sitting in the car with Sandra, I had felt I was someone special, I couldn't wait for her next visit to take me out again.

The following Saturday Sandra decided to take me to her parents home around 15 miles away in a small village on the outskirts of Leicestershire. As we approached the house, I was apprehensive, taking a long time getting out the car, and dragging my feet on the slabs walking down the side footpath of the house to the backdoor. Sandra pushed it open and went through. My first sight of her Mum was of a small lady bending down to put some laundry into a washing machine, realising she had visitors, she popped up like a Jack in the Box saying, "Hello."

I said, "Hi," and stood to the side whilst she bustled by me to put the kettle on. I was surprised, whilst Sandra was of a big build and about 5 foot 10; her Mum stood about 5 feet 2 and had dark curly brown hair and brown eyes. Sandra was 23 years old and her Mum looked in her fifties. She took charge straight away, telling me to go and take a seat in the lounge. Checking my shoes were clean I tiptoed through to a large room with a rusty coloured carpet and a huge bright cream settee. I sat down disappearing into the corner of it. I politely thanked Sandra's Mum as she brought me a cup of tea and a biscuit. She seemed ok and after a while I started to relax, it was an hour or so later when Sandra's Dad arrived, he walked into the room and sat down to watch the horseracing. He grinned across at me a few times and kept offering me the biscuit tin, although he still didn't say much, I warmed to him straight away and was sorry when it was time for us to go.

The trips to Sandra's parents became so regular I nicknamed them my Saturday Mum and Dad. I really felt part of their family and my own must have been fed up with me ranting and raving what a fantastic time I had at their house. Sandra's Mum had a big sense of humour and she made me laugh, as when she really started to laugh, she would have to dash to the toilet. She also had a very dominant side and I was stunned at the arguments she would have with Sandra's Dad.

The first time I was sitting quietly in their lounge watching the wrestling, when I heard raised voices, and it wasn't just the odd shout, there was so much emotion in their voices, that it upset me, Sandra came into the lounge and found me upset. I could not explain but the shouting seemed to rebound from the walls and I felt I had done something terribly wrong. The next thing I knew was Sandra's Mum coming in and putting her arms around me to tell me that it was ok, and to take no notice of them. Sandra's Dad followed through with a cup of tea for me and some chocolate biscuits. They were so together, which had seemed impossible to me, ten minutes back. Again, I was at a bit of a loss for although I had been upset, now I was having the time of my life with three adults all fussing over me. It was a bit confusing as the emotions seemed to rocket from one end to the other. I was shielded from shouting at home, as Mum and Dads philosophy was not in front of the kids, this also extended to their passion for one another, so it was very rare to see them embrace at any time.

As the time passed, I grew fonder and fonder of Sandra and her Mum and Dad, and although I loved my own parents dearly, I looked forward to the weekends. Sandra also got to know my family better and her relationship as well as being my Mum's boss at work extended to family friend. She particularly got on well with my Nan, my Mum's Mum, and we had some great times where we took my Nan out for the day in the car. My Nan was in her eighties. She was a lovely lady with a kind heart and a terrific sense of humour. Sandra and I took it upon ourselves to look after her. We both spent hours doing up my Nan's house, trying to keep it warm for her, and taking her out when we could.

Sandra would often help me with my homework and she got to know my best friend Susanne well. I had been to infant school with Susanne and now at the age of 12 we were still in the same class. Susanne had two younger brothers and unfortunately a family where the male species dominated, and it was at this cost that she was often required to stay at home and keep her Mum company.

Denny and I were always doing deals with each other, I would make up a story and tell it to her at night if she did routine housework jobs for me. As Mum worked in the mornings, we would often try to put the washing out for her or bring it in. I loved Mum dearly and it was a natural part of me to want to help. Jane on the other hand was born to be waited upon and in turn, she grew to resent the younger kid sister who was so helpful, as it put her nose out of joint. She was two and half years older than me and was very sophisticated, she was very intelligent and did not have to work hard to get results. She also took great pride in her appearance and wore clothes that I would not feel comfortable in, as they were so smart. I would feel like being in my Sunday best, where you walked round not daring to put a foot wrong. Denny on the other hand was like me, the scruffier the more comfortable.

I did not know what my sisters thought of Sandra; they both had best friends and were too busy in their own little worlds to take much notice of what I did. Sandra started to do some serious talking with me. Gradually introducing me to an area, which had been out of bounds at home and not mentioned. She started quite casually asking if I minded looking different to the rest of my family. She referred to the fact that I looked so much like her and her Mum; they both had dark eyes and brown hair. I thought of the book and the story Mum and Dad told me when I was little. It was about when they wanted children; I understood that they tried to have children and the Dr told Mum that she would not be able to. Therefore, Mum and Dad went to a children's home, looking at all these babies. Jane shared the same birthday as Mum and they accepted it as a positive message that she was meant for them. A few months later, they adopted her into their family.

Jane had blue eyes and mousey coloured hair, everybody adored her and my Mum and Dad were very happy. A couple of years later they decided they would like another daughter so that Jane would have a sister to play with. This time when they went to the home, they told me that a baby lay quietly, staring at them with beautiful big dark brown eyes. They went and looked at some other babies but this one was so quiet you had to peer over the cot to make sure there was a baby there, and a pair of nearly black eyes gazed back. They adopted me three months later. Sandra interrupted the tale and asked, "What about Denny?"

As I was relating this back to Andrea, I paused, finding it difficult, Andrea smiled, "Come on, carry on."

"I responded relating the rest of the tale, "Denny is Mum and Dad's, after they had accepted they couldn't have children and were happily settled with Jane and I, my Mum found out she was expecting and along came Denny. She had brilliant blue eyes and was blonde. My Dad used to be blonde when he was a lad. Jane could pass as Mum and Dad's and credit due to my parents, not many people know that my elder sister and I are adopted." Sandra looked across at me saying, "Don't you mind?" I looked at her and felt uncomfortable. I loved my family. I was

not going to let anyone tamper with any cracks. I did not give Sandra the chance of delving anymore and quickly changed the subject to something else.

That night I tossed and turned, I knew that deep down I yearned to be part of my parents, I wanted my Mum to look like me, I wished that I had come out of her womb. I wondered what my real Mum looked like. I wished that I were as brave as my younger sister was. She was so popular, and when visitors came, she was the extrovert. I hid under my bed, if I had to come out I would go and sit on the floor next to the visitor I liked. If I really liked them, I would push up close to their ankles trying to be close, but not intrusive. I hadn't the guts to sit next to them, I felt safer on the floor.

Our bedroom faced down the drive and you could see the cars drive over the car park towards our village. I got into a habit of looking for Sandra's car about 8.30am before school and any time between 4.15 and 5pm after school. On spotting her car, I would lift the net curtain and wave and she would raise a hand or flash the indicators. After school, I would sometimes stop at my friend Susanne's house and we would play games like hot rice with her brother.

Sometimes when I played at Susanne's I would spot Sandra sitting in her car in the roadway opposite. Susanne would ask me why she was there and I would reply that I did not know. My house was just under 10 minutes away from Susanne's by bicycle, I would pedal through the back roads through the churchyard which I hated to do in the dark, across the green around the corner, and I was home. I used my bike a lot and became a master of arts on it.

As Susanne stayed home a lot, I did a lot of drawing at home and I liked to do woodwork, both my Grandpa's were good with wood and I made a bird box which I hung on the fence outside my window. It was successful and year after year I had a pair of blue tits use it.

Sometimes I would see Sandra after school in the week and she got on so well with my Nan, that she moved in to my Nan's big house and helped with the bills. I thought it was good she was there as I felt there was someone there for my Nan who had lost her husband a couple of years back.

Sandra took my Nan to see her Mum and Dad and they grew very fond of her. Nan always had a good sense of humour and enjoyed the visits, it was like *an outing for her. I grew fond of Sandra's Dad and he took an interest in me, showing me how to do the job he was doing. He was very clever and I learnt to do various practical jobs, such as simple electrics to plastering and laying floorboards. I liked to be practical and this was great as I felt I was contributing to helping a family, who had taken me in as one of their own."*

Andrea commented, "I can see how your Mum and Dad might have felt a little bit jealous." I shrugged, raising my eyebrows and continued.

"The weeks passed and soon it was to be Sandra's Mum's 50th, as a surprise for her and her Dad, Sandra and her brother arranged a secret trip to Sweden for them. I was in on the secret and it was such a happy moment when they found out they were going. Sandra's Mum got all soppy, having to dash to the bathroom, because she was crying, rather than laughing. The weekend they were due to fly, Sandra and I would take them to the bus station in London.

As I was only 12, Sandra asked my parents if they would mind if I slept over at her parents' house because we would be back late. They were happy to oblige and I looked forward to that weekend.

The weekend came; it was a cold crisp day with bright sunshine. Sandra's Mum was nervous as she had not flown before and her Dad was busy leaving notes for jobs that needed attending. It was a good trip down to London and arriving early, we bought a cup of coffee smelling more of the polystyrene cup than of coffee, but it was wet and warm. The bus driver came and everyone hustled forward to put their luggage in the hold, we gave Sandra's parents a hug and started our journey back.

Once we arrived back at their house, Sandra took my bag containing my pyjamas and put them into her parent's room, "We're sleeping in here tonight," she told me. I nodded feeling apprehensive, as I thought I was having a different room, but then my thoughts turned to my Nan's, where often when we stayed there I would share a bed with both my sisters. We would have bolsters down the bed and fall asleep having fights over them. I tiptoed down stairs and curled up on the cream sofa with a mug of hot chocolate. Sandra cooked steak and chips. I sat eating, watching the television feeling good and cosy. I leaned against Sandra, with my feet up whilst she read her book.

It was about 10.30pm when I said I was going to bed. Sandra gave me a kiss, saying she would be up in a bit. I went upstairs and changed into my pyjamas, having had a wash in the bathroom and cleaned my teeth. I climbed into the big bed, which seemed enormous. I was tired, but still I scanned the room for unknown shadows and open wardrobe doors, any apprehensions drifted away as I fell asleep. It was a while later when I became aware of someone hugging me. I sleepily, nestled into the warmth hollow of the mattress. I was still half-asleep. I dreamt I felt someone rubbing my back and it was a nice feeling.

The next thing I realised was a hand creeping under my pyjamas, rubbing my back covering more and more area. I felt uncomfortable, not sure, what was happening. I dreamt I was rolling onto my back; I could now feel moving fingers over my breasts that were just starting to form. I was confused and didn't dare move, so scared I couldn't open my eyes, I tried to hold my breath, hardly daring to breathe as each movement was leading to consequences. Sandra breathing heavily, now caressing my face, panted, "You're gorgeous, and I want to paint you." Now awake, I stared up at the ceiling. I felt her hand rubbing over my breasts, and her fingers were going around in little circles, each lap they seemed to tighten around my nipples, looming out of nowhere, forming little hard peaks. Excited, she leant over kissing them, biting them gently, sucking them like a newborn babe cradled to its mother. I froze unable to move or talk, feeling a million miles away. Her hands, now travelling down from my breasts, were tucking under the waistband of my pyjamas.

I opened my eyes staring at the ceiling, feeling her hand rubbing against me, starting off very gentle then each stroke or caress seemed to travel more, and harder and faster, I could hear her moaning and then I jumped with pain, as her fingers entered me. My racing thoughts were confused. I could only see black, feeling fingers closing over my hand casting me into a place that I did not know was possible. Little wiry hairs between my fingers, making me shudder. Then, my fingers forced into a hot and sticky place. I could not breathe, my fingers, slimy and wet. Suddenly I was on the ceiling and I was looking down, I saw this big person lean over and give this tiny person a kiss on the cheek then the large person got out of the bed and left the room.

When I woke up in the morning, I got up quickly, and dressed, Sandra was in the kitchen making a coffee, "Hi, sleepy head," she smiled, "Do you want tea or coffee?" I chose tea and sat down to drink it, Sandra was reading her book, so I got mine out, we had such a normal day that I thought I had dreamt the previous night and I buried it deep down.

Sandra helped me with my homework. She questioned me, about my Mum and Dad. She was nice and asked if I minded that Mum preferred Denny to me, and how did I manage to put up with Jane being so lazy? She pointed out that it was wrong for my Mum to give preference to Denny, and I tried to argue back for my Mum's sake, saying it was understandable because Denny was Mum's.

I had grown up to accept that when we shifted through family photographs, that Mum would spend twice as long looking at the ones with Denny on, and that the nice one or super one would be of Denny. I had also accepted that there would be more photos of Denny everywhere. It did hurt deep down, but I chose not to go down that path, yet with Sandra's persistence, I started to feel the hurt and with the hurt grew resentment. Also with the resentment grew a yearning to find my real Mum, I'd already pictured my Mum she would be like mine except she would have a darker skin, dark brown eyes and very dark brown hair. I pictured her perfect in every way.

Sandra's persistence in feeding negative pieces of information about my family started to have a bigger effect than I would have felt possible. I started to look for faults and I started to be on my guard. At the same time because I was feeling and seeing negative issues at home, I started to see the advantages of being spoilt and looked after, I noticed the special attention I received from Sandra, she took a huge interest in my homework, she got to know Susanne and spoilt her as well.

I had shown Andrea my writing on Sandra, as I could not verbalise what had happened. Andrea asked me to try to continue and not give up.

CHAPTER 15

Grooming

Sandra continued to take me out; I loved her parents and liked the special attention I received. Somehow, she always had time for me, and my thoughts and actions seemed important to her. She had a soft spot for my Nan and it was a relief for someone else to look after and care for her. I know my Mum loved my Nan, but sometimes I think she was too close to see that my Nan was ageing and was not as active as she used to be.

It was inevitable that my parents started to feel uneasy about the amount of time Sandra was spending with my Nan and I, also they were against the fact that Sandra moved in with Nan. They were worried that my Nan might lose any benefits she was entitled to. Some unpleasant conversations took place. Sandra moved out to a house she managed to buy nearby, I was upset over the move. It seemed easier to know my Nan was not alone if anything should happen, I adjusted to the move and I accepted it, but deep down I thought Mum was jealous that her Boss and close friend, spent more time with her Mum and her daughter.

I started to see cracks in my family and instead of healing; they seemed to get longer and deeper. In turn, I felt alone and started to depend more and more on Sandra. She helped me with my homework, and looked after Nan, she helped decorate Nan's house, she took my Nan out, and she seemed to listen to me. In addition, her Mum and Dad were great and I turned increasingly to their direction. Susanne was also finding her Mum needed her. I still loved my family, *yet as I turned into my teens, Jane was a sophisticated 15 going on twenty. Denny had a good friend and spent more time at her friends' house, Mum and Dad were always busy and I grabbed any attention I could get.*

Sandra's house was situated on a main road, it was a 2 up and 2 down, she bought it for a low price, and it needed attention to it. Her Dad was the perfect man for the job. He was a plumber, but knew many other aspects of the building trade. I relished in the work and I loved to help as much as possible, enjoying the new challenges it would bring.

The house was on the Green and you could see across to the church from the front windows. It was half way between Susanne's house and home. I could cycle to it in 5 minutes and it was next door to the local shop.

I was not enjoying school and I was not alone, that year all students went on strike for more discipline. The teachers would lean back in their chairs; heels crossed on desks and tell you not to disturb them. They also insisted on first name terms, if you did not turn up for a lesson, it did not matter.

I hated school; the only sessions I liked were the art lessons and sport. I was like a big kid at break, bringing a tennis ball for myself, and a big gang, to play hot rice or rounders. Sometimes I would look to the gate and see Sandra parked up the road. I never questioned it, as I had my bicycle and whilst at school I was in a different world with my friends.

Today it was Saturday morning and I was ready for a hard days work doing up the house. Sandra's Dad, was already there, and he nodded to me from the top of the ladder. He was putting up new guttering and I immediately eyed the black plastic bits wondering if he would want me to put any together.

My first job was to run over to the bread shop and buy some newly baked rolls. I ran across to the Green and queued patiently, the smell of newly baked bread made every second waiting worthwhile.

"Hi, can I have a dozen rolls please?" The woman smiled at me as she passed the bag over, I smiled back, and she knew Mum.

Back in the long narrow kitchen, I watched Sandra frying the tinned tomatoes, smelling the great aroma of smoky bacon, which wafted outside to her Dad. He finished the piece he was doing and came down to tuck in. I loved these rolls, the tomatoes oozed out, when you took a bite, and the mixture of real butter and bacon made me want to eat more. I took a sip of my coffee and listened whilst Sandra's Dad gave instructions for us to carry on plastering in the corner of the kitchen.

We worked hard that day, the time whizzed by, Sandra's Dad left at around 5pm, and I went into the front room. I sat on the settee, covered by a dark chocolate bedspread. I decided Sandra liked dark brown because her bathroom suite was dark brown, and had a thick cream carpet.

I curled up on the settee and started to watch the TV. Sandra came in and brought me a drink. I sipped it slowly, clasping the mug for warmth. She pulled the thick red velvet curtains across, and the room went very dark. She switched on two little lamps and I looked at the African figures on the mantelpiece. She played Simon and Garfunkels 'Bridge over TroubledWater' then she went upstairs, and came down with a photo of her fiancé. He had died and I could tell from her expressions and her mood that it was going to be a difficult evening. Some days she would just sit and sob her eyes out, I would feel helpless and would try to comfort her, yet I felt inadequate and somewhat embarrassed.

Today I was praying in my head repeatedly that she would not get the pills out, sometimes she would take some out and threaten to take them. I would sit and cradle her like a little baby saying any comforting words I could think of. I would make her a drink and try to tell her that the world was a good place. It was hard but it was easier than when she went out. Those nights were terrifying, the first time I was so scared, she drove so fast, and it was late. I had no idea where we were going but she knew where.We ended up at a place called Beacon Hill, a remote wilderness, I climbed the hill with her and watched whilst she faced the wind and looked out across the views. I felt scared, I walked over to her and grabbed her arm, and it was as if I was not there.

Slowly she walked to the edge of the rocks and looked down, now I was not only scared, I was petrified. I wanted to be at home, tucked up in bed. Reality was, I was out on the top of a wilderness watching someone I cared about in pain, not knowing whether they were going to jump. It seemed hours later when I was so cold I could not feel my feet. I was just so relieved that we were going home and that I was not looking at a corpse.

Anyway, I was not at the Beacon, or on any bridge, overlooking motorways, I was here and at least it felt safer than out. Sandra started to talk again, telling me that she and Tim were going to have twins, that they were both going to have dark curly hair and deep brown eyes, "Like yours," she told me, she turned to me and I felt so sad. The tears were still damp and our roles were changed, I felt I had to protect her. I listened as she told me repeatedly how much she loved him. Exhausted, as I had worked hard all day, and feeling worried, I turned to her, "Look let me ring your Mum up?" Sandra shook her head, "Please let me tell your Mum," I was nearly begging.

"No, please, trust me no-one must know, promise me," she pulled my face up, so I was looking straight into her eyes, gently she caressed my hair. I snuggled down into the corner of the settee; I could not think straight, I was already concerned over my Nan's health. This was a different ball game, I felt heavy with it. I felt sad and I wanted my Mum. I wanted my real Mum; I had a wanting in me to find her. I wanted someone to look after me, I wished I was like my younger sister and had come out my Mum's womb, perhaps then she would have had more time for me. I lay back and cuddled the cushion, listening to Mrs. Robinson. I half fell asleep and then I felt her cuddle me. I did not mind, I wanted someone to give me a big hug.

She was rubbing my back, and I again started to drift. In my mind, I was in with the music, I was the snail, and I could hear I'd rather be a snail. I could feel the heavy weight on me. Was it the house, I was carrying? Why couldn't I move? Snails cannot move fast. The weight got heavier and heavier and as the pain got to excruciating, I felt the black coming...

The cold water made me gasp and I just stopped my legs from buckling, Sandra was holding me under my arms, and I smiled as I tried to show I was ok. She let go of me and I immediately slumped down, I was a snail I had no legs, and then as the strength came back I stood up. She turned the shower off and held a big warm towel up. She wrapped it round me and cuddled me; I followed her downstairs and sat sipping hot chocolate. As the warmth came through, the life seemed to seep through my body, and I was back, it was I. Sandra smiled as she passed my clothes warm from the radiator. I pulled my jeans and sweatshirt on.

All I wanted to do was to go to sleep. Sandra passed my coat, and together we walked down the street to my house. A couple of times, my legs gave way, sometimes I would have to sit and wait, other times I just stood and carried on. As I reached my gate Sandra said, "Bye." I turned giving her a kiss on the cheek and then ran shakily up the drive. Once near the bungalow I tiptoed round, quietly placed the key in the back door, and let myself in. I crept through to the bedroom, changed, and slipped into bed.

Andrea asked, "Were you always under the shower?" I stared; I could not answer or even go near the question. Andrea continued, "I guess that was the easiest way for her to bring you round and it gave her a buzz to put freezing cold water on you." I did not answer.

The days passed fast and they grew into weeks, and the weeks seemed to pass to months, soon I was ready to take my exams, it was tough at school. My life had dropped and besides school, which was an all time low I spent my spare time seeing Sandra. I felt I was unwanted as Sandra kept reminding me how my Mum adored my younger sister, and Mum without meaning to, kept reinstating this, telling Denny she was beautiful and having a lot more interest in her younger daughter.

It was not big things, but even when I asked for something it would depend on Denny's reaction first. I started to think about searching for my real Mum, and Sandra encouraged me.

Sandra asked about homework, encouraged my sport, which was badminton as my Dad used to play, and gave me the hugs that I needed. I learnt to block out the pain and feelings. Anything bad I suppressed, including when Sandra was suicidal. The times I was on motorway bridges trying to pull on to her jumper, inside, I was screaming out for help, yet on the outside, I was fine I had to be.

Today I was in the bathroom and I looked at myself in the mirror, I felt ill, I hated myself so much I felt low, and I felt hopeless. Tired from trying to help Sandra, I felt a massive pressure and it would not go away. I lifted my right arm and clenched my fist and I aimed at my face. I did not feel the blows I just hit and hit and hit. I came out of the bathroom and tried to think of an excuse for the massive black eye that had started to appear. My face started to hurt and I came up with the idea that I had slipped and caught my face on the side of the table. I walked into the kitchen, Mum was busy making sandwiches so she did not notice, but as Dad turned from the sink, he said, "What have you done to your face?" coming to have a closer look.

"Does it show, I just slipped and caught the table?" I muttered, Mum came towards me and put some butter on it. If anything, it made it look worse but she said it would help.

Sandra was concerned when she saw my face, but I lied to her as well. As I looked in the mirror, I did not see the overall picture, I focused on my bruise, the blacker it was, the more satisfaction I felt.

I still went with Sandra to see her parents and I grew very fond of them. I loved my own family and somehow the more I loved them, the more little things would hurt. I spent a lot of time with my dogs and bird watching. School time was worse, there was a lot of pressure to do well, and my parents started to ask what I wanted to do when I left school.

Jane had a good job as a secretary and my Mum and Dad were pushing for a direction for me. The truth was all I loved was my dogs and being outside. I asked if I could go and work at the kennels. Dad said, "What on earth do you want to do that for? There's enough work here with our dogs and there is no future in it," I tried every angle.

They suggested vet school, but I was too soft, I knew I could never end a life, even if it meant putting an animal out of its misery, and I also knew I would become over emotional, worrying about the different animals health.

Today was Saturday. I cycled up to see Sandra, I had come to a decision and wanted her to know first. I had my own key and let myself in, "Hi," I said, and I continued excitedly, "I have decided I am going to stay on at school, and then I can do 'A' level art etc." I was expecting Sandra to be happy at this, but she shrugged her shoulders and told me that I was making a mistake. "That school is rubbish, half the teachers don't care, don't waste your life there Bridget, go and get a job," she turned to go into the kitchen, I followed her, my world all shook up again. "But I don't know what I want," I replied.

"Well, what are you good at?" She looked at me whilst handing me a coffee. "I like doing maths and I am good at it, and I like writing and drawing, but I want to be outside." Sandra sat down on the settee and passed a coaster for me to put my drink on, I sat down and started to think again, "Mum and Dad want me to apply for a job at the Bank because Mum used to work in one," I wrinkled my nose at the thought. "But that would be quite well paid and I know for a fact you can finish around 4pm," replied Sandra. This appealed as it was not a lot later than school time. I went and fetched the phone directory to start to look at the addresses of local banks. I arrived home, resigned to the idea that a bank would be an ok place to work, and asked Dad to help me write out some applications. I didn't know what results I'd get, but I knew I was taking 8 'O' levels and that I needed 4 to get into the bank.

I asked at school for a reference and my tutor gave me a brilliant one, saying I was in all the top classes and predicted to achieve top results at all subjects. Armed with the reference, I wrote and waited. The first one to invite me to an interview was the Midland, and although I had a good presentation, they refused to take me on until I had the results of my exams.

The end of term came and I was in a mess, I felt under pressure, Sandra was becoming worse. Her moods were so bad that she scared Susanne, who had witnessed her, slamming doors, and smoking non-stop. She had also seen her crying uncontrollably, leaving me feeling embarrassed. I was spending time after school at Sandra's, and I was spending all weekends there. I lost count how many times I woke up under the shower, or how many times I had tried desperately to cheer her up, telling her life was worth living. I was in an automatic mode; all I could think about was finding my real Mum.

At home, there was increasing conflict as Jane had started to go out more, and was coming back the worse for wear under the influence of alcohol. There were continuous rows between her and Mum and I could not believe how lazy she had become. I wanted to try to protect Mum, so I was continually making the drinks Jane demanded, and continually cleaning up after her. Deep down I resented it, but I did not like to see Mum sit down after working all day and then rise to her feet, because my older sister wanted something. Dad told Jane off, but Jane seemed to have a chip on her shoulder, and every time she was reprimanded, the chip became bigger.

Denny stayed at her friends' a lot, and I started to spend as much time as possible at Sandra's taking my dog Judy with me when I could.

My Dad's nephew had a boys' home in the Ardennes, and he invited me over in the summer holidays. I grabbed the chance, persuading Susanne to come with me. Our initial reunion with my cousin ended in tragedy.We greeted him warmly on the building site where he was building a new home. Unfortunately, his young son toddled off, whilst everyone was greeting each other, and fell in a large puddle. He was too young to get up and with his medical problems, drowned in a few inches of water.We were all heart broken, and I felt a massive surge of guilt as I had walked up holding his hand, and he had been laughing with me.

When Susanne and I arrived back in England, no one mentioned the accident. I could not cope. I went round to see Sandra. She was not there and I remembered her saying she was away for a few days with a friend.When Sandra got back, I was surprised at how worried she seemed. She sat me down on the settee and started to play 'Bridge Over Troubled Water' the words got to me, and she stroked my hair telling me that I should not be ashamed and I should be upset about his death. She could not understand why no one had talked about it. She wanted me to talk about it and discuss it. I did not want to talk about it.

In the dark she was nice and as her words got softer I started to feel a little of the pain for my cousins baby, yet as the pain started and her arms and hands started to target my body, my mind numbed again and I was in my world away from any feeling or pain that existed.

The summer came and went and I could not relax. I was on a mission and I did not know what the mission was about, I just knew I worried like mad for my Nan. I worried about Sandra, who was so unpredictable and suicidal. I saw a very vulnerable person underneath, who though could be so violent and moody, also tugged at my heartstrings. I hated seeing anyone be so hurt or upset.

I received a letter in the post to say that I had been successful with a job application with another Bank, but I needed a medical for them to accept me. My Mum and Dad were so proud. I was apprehensive, yet pleased that I had a possible job. My medical was booked for in September in Leicester. I didn't know beforehand that a medical was needed, and I was alarmed because when I'd returned from Belgium, I'd taken my Dad's razor out of his case and used it on my arms and legs. I had started to do it in the spring before. One day I was so numb with everything I needed something to take the other feeling away, and that something had to be strong. I understood why some people turned to drink. I wanted to bash my face, but having done it several times, it was not enough. I needed the relief and without planning it, I went into the bathroom and locked the door. As I gazed in the mirror, it just did not seem worth hitting my face, I saw Dad's razor, and I do not know how I started, but I pulled it against my skin and I hardly felt anything. Nevertheless, I got a great deal of satisfaction at seeing the red trickle of blood that was starting to run from the line. It made me feel better, so I did another and another. Soon my arm was covered and I needed more space, so I rolled up my trouser leg and started on my legs. They were not deep cuts, but deep enough to be noticed. However, my jeans concealed them. I wore cardigans.

When seen, I said the puppies had scratched me. That summer even when it was hot, I wore my cardigan, and Mum must have noticed but never commented. Now I had a medical, I wondered how I was going to explain my arms. Mum had the answer, "Tell the Dr that you were picking gooseberries," she said. At the medical, he did ask me and I remembered what Mum had said, so I repeated it. I passed the medical to start work in October, at a bank in Leicester.

CHAPTER 16

Chemical Straight Jacket

I had written as much as I could at the time about my past, and Dr Lynn decided in October to let me go home, with weekly visits as an outpatient and 24-hour fast track admission. I returned home and tried to catch up on lost time with my family. Dr Lynn had warned me that recovery would be slow, and he was right. I had already been diagnosed with posttraumatic stress disorder alongside other complex labels. My latest revelation about Sandra had shocked many of the professionals working with me.

I soon discovered that my feelings of the past were thought to be inappropriate. If anyone asked me about Sandra, or the Bank Manager, I could describe how he or she had helped me and cared for me. I was relating to my needs at the time, and because my mind had suppressed the unwanted, all I could relate to was the positive events.

Although I was home, I was still surviving on a knife-edge. It was the support and stability of my visits to the hospital that helped keep my life as normal as possible. In the next few months, I was to find out in a cruel way, that as soon as I started to relax and have a good time and enjoy life at home, I would experience severe and life threatening flashbacks. It caused upheaval and distress to Joseph and my children. I had been offered medication. I had seen the effect of medication on some of the patients, and I always argued I would prefer a life with risks than no life at all. A time came when I had no choice.

Joseph was away at a wine tasting. I drove Jo Jo to school and had Tee Jay with me. Driving home, I knew I was struggling. I was agitated and had been fighting to stay okay. I suffered from intense periods of despair where my mind told me to run and escape. I could never recall a reason why. It was as if I needed a release.

In the past the actual escaping from hospital had caused huge adrenalin rushes, and the irrational behaviour of acting out, such as jumping off motorway bridges or attempting to jump at the train station had boosted the adrenalin rush giving me a temporary release. When I started to feel bad, a simple action like a telephone call to the hospital could keep me okay as it was a diversion, and sometimes would succeed long enough for me to get past the impulsivity stage of needing a release.

Other times, trying to keep busy or engage with someone was not enough. When the impulsivity took over I was escaping from a black hole, consequential behaviour was impulsive and not thought through.

When I started to feel bad, I fought with all resources possible to stay ok until the danger period had passed. Usually the very fact of being in company of someone else kept me grounded. Everyday routine was good for me. Today I knew I was not managing and after denying it for a week, knew it was building to an unhealthy level. I rang Andrea up and she told me to see her at 4pm. The drawback was I had to wait until four o'clock and had to take both children.

I did my best to struggle through the day and I picked up a leaflet selling books by mail. The description of a particular book caught my eye, as the contents seemed so extreme. It was a book about god's brother being a rapist and it was so extreme, it attracted me to reading more of it. I was not drawn enough to buy it, but it left me with a sick feeling.

Later as I ran up the steps to the hospital and the receptionist kept an eye on the children. I was disturbed to see another consultant with Andrea, but it was too late to run from the room. I was also desperate for help. I sat down and tried to answer the questions asked by Dr Libber and Andrea. Dr Libber was nice. She was petite with dark hair and attractive with presence, firm, but kind and did not intimidate me.

As I had struggled all day, I concentrated hard focusing on the book details, I read earlier. This unfortunately did me no favours, as I turned to Dr Libber and said, "If he was a rapist, it wouldn't do me any good up there would it?" I was reflecting from the book I had read and being honest about how I was feeling and revealing that if I did kill myself, and the book was true, I would be in a further mess. I told Andrea and Dr Libber, Joseph was away. He was returning late. I told them my parents were in Australia on holiday and my sister was away. The options turned to Andrea and Dr Libber talking about admitting me to hospital and social services, taking the kids. I had not anticipated this and it scared me. I left the room whilst they discussed arrangements. When I went into the waiting room, the receptionist had gone, as it was past five and a nurse was looking after the children. She told me she finished at five and was going to go in, to ask to finish. She disappeared through the doorway to Dr Libber and Andrea.

I took my chance. I ran over to my children, "Come on," I whispered. I grabbed their coats, picking Tee Jay up in my arms and holding Jo Jo's hand; I quickly ran through the door and headed down the stairs full pelt. My instincts were to drive fast, but I needed to make sure the children were safe first. I then jumped into the drivers' seat and sped off. I expected Andrea to come rushing over the car park, but she did not. I drove fast and headed towards home. My mind was racing and I tried to think what to do. I could not go home; I knew the police would come. My parents and sister were away, my friends would not understand, as they did not know my circumstances, I was alone. I tried to rationalise things desperately whizzing around in my head.

The main thing was to look after the children. They were both hungry so I headed to a nearby McDonalds where I knew I could get something hot inside them. As they both sat eating and drinking, I started to panic. I did not know where to turn. I needed somewhere safe and remote to think things over and decide how I was going to handle the situation. I decided to go to Switherland Woods. I knew it was getting late so there should not be too many people. I could take the children for a short walk and decide what to do.

Tee Jay had finished his meal; Jo Jo said she felt sick, "Oh, darling," I said, "Come here for a cuddle." She sat on my knee and as I talked to her, I felt her head, she was not hot. I put her sickly feeling down to rushing and thought a nice short walk would make us all feel better. I paid the bill and walked out with both children.

I headed for Switherland Woods, pulling into the car park in the woods. There were a couple of other cars there. As I dressed the children and zipped their coats up, the occupants of one car headed off. I was about to get out of our car, when a man who was dressed quite shabby came out of the distance and headed towards the car parked near us, because it was remote I decided to wait until he drove off. He did not, and came up to our car staring through the window. I put the automatic lock on and as I turned to the children, my mobile rang, it was the hospital ward manager, and I always liked him.

"Hello Bridget, where are you?" He asked, "Are the children with you?" He must have known they were because Jo Jo took Tee Jay's sweet from him and Tee Jay started to yell. "Hi, both children are ok; we are just going for a walk." I answered trying to sound as if I was completely in control.

"Where are you?" Ian asked again. The children were making a right noise arguing over the rest of the sweets. I still had not answered when Ian asked. "Are you in the woods?"

I hesitated, as a rule I was an honest person, part of me wanted to tell him, but I did not want to be found. Yet, I also did not want them to spend time searching for me, "Look, ok I'm in the woods and yes, it is the one with the quarry and I don't want any fuss, we are all ok." I put the phone down, not wishing to continue the conversation, yet it rang again and my conscience would not let me ignore it. I did not get chance to sort the kids out and Jo Jo had taken most of the sweets and would not let Tee Jay have his McDonald toy back. "Hello," I answered reluctantly, it was not Ian, it was Barbara, a nurse in her late fifties, who held your hand and was very patronising. Her care was extreme; sometimes it could be brilliant and other times not so good. I always believed she meant well. "Hello Bridget, what are you doing to those poor children?" It was a statement, not a question.

It was just then I could hear a helicopter and looking up could see some *bright lights shining through the now dusky evening. "Why's there lights up there, what's it doing?" I was half talking to myself, yet Barbara took over and put words into my mouth. "You can see lights above you, no it's not a space ship, are those children alright?" I realised that they were worried about my children who were fine except for arguing, as I stared into the sky. I could make out a helicopter that was circling. The other man had gone and I had not noticed. We were alone except for this helicopter, "I have to go, bye." I switched the phone off and then put it on again. I quickly got both the children out and making sure, they were wrapped up warm, headed off the nearest footpath.*

I did not know what I was doing, but I did not want the children taken off me. The light was fading and the ground was muddy. I knew the woods well and headed deeper into the middle...

I paused from my writing. I hated this and still had bad flashbacks every time I heard a helicopter. I continued, as I had been told to write down events in hospital or out.

The phone rang again. It was Ian. "Bridget, can you see the police helicopter?" I could only just hear him.

"Yes, it's circling above me," I yelled.

"Well go out and wave to them," said Ian. I hung up, I knew they were all out to get me and I decided to dash deep into the woods for cover. I thought of the quarry, and it seemed comforting to be able to familiarise myself with a place I knew well. I put the phone into my pocket. I picked Tee Jay up and held Jo Jo's hand, "Are you ok darling?" I asked her.

"Yes Mummy, can we walk now?" asked Jo Jo clinging on to my hand tightly, Tee Jay made noises pointing up to the helicopter. "Yes, that's a helicopter isn't it?" I said to Tee Jay. I squeezed Jo Jo's hand and we made our way further into the woods. I tried to hurry as it was getting darker and I wanted to find somewhere safe for us to rest. The helicopter seemed to be moving away, yet it kept coming back and then moving again. I was thinking of the heat seeking equipment they had on board and wondered what it would look like. I walked quickly and started to get scared, as the light was fading extremely fast. I came to a steep hill, and years of experience told me to move to the left a bit and then

walk up it. I did helping Jo Jo. Once we got to the top, I decided to look back into the distance to see if I could still see our car.

When I looked back, I was shocked. I could see numerous police cars, vans and a police bike. Oh, no, I thought, I wondered if I could delay them, then Joseph might have got back, and the children would not be taken into social services. "Come on," I shouted to Jo Jo, "Let's run down the hill." Jo Jo laughed and holding my hand, she led the way. We could not go too fast as it was steep in places. At the bottom the footpath forked, I took the left one and had to stop as a bramble had caught Jo Jo's woolly tights. "Mummy," she cried. "It's alright darling, it's just a nasty weed, let me get it off you." I bent down and gently lifted off the sharp thorns and rubbed her leg. "Do you want a lift too?" I said. She nodded; with all the energy I could muster, I lifted both children off the ground.

We headed off again and at the next steep bit, we again tried to look back. This time I could not see anything. It was about ten minutes later when we heard a noise and looking behind us, we could see a police officer with his dog, "Down," he shouted. I was so nervous I did not know if he meant the dog or me. I bent down and pretended to do up my shoelace. "It's alright," he called. "Are you ok?" I nodded. He kept his distance, the dog was barking like mad. Jo Jo cuddled up to me. "Wait there, don't move," said the police officer. He was only young and smiled. I stood up, both children were staring at the dog, it was barking loudly. The helicopter shone a welcome beam down, and soon other police came through the bracken towards us. Two of the men offered to help carry the children, and I was glad, my arms ached like mad. I had not realised how far into the woods we were.

It was difficult making our way back, the helicopter pilot radioed and kindly volunteered to shine his search beams down lighting the way. When we eventually arrived back at the car park, the police asked me to sit in the back of their car and the children sat either side of me. I hugged them; they were fine and seemed to be enjoying the adventure.

The police officer in the passenger seat turned out to be the inspector and man in charge. He spoke kindly as he turned round to face me, "We've decided to take you back to the police station; you can warm up there, whilst we sort things out." He smiled and I felt a bit better.

Once inside the station we sat down in a lounge area. A police woman was assigned to look after me, some of the other police officers went by, and they all seemed to be in good spirits and teasing each other, over the amount of mud on their trousers. I kept apologising. They kept laughing it off. The police woman joked as the Inspector handed me a mug of hot steaming tea, "It's not everyday, you get a mug of tea made by the Inspector." We all laughed, including the Inspector himself.

Another police officer brought over some orange squash for the children and they made them some bowls of cornflakes. It was now past ten at night and both children were tired. The Inspector told me Joseph was coming in, and I had to wait to see the police, Dr and a social worker. I immediately knew that meant sectioning. I was so relieved that Joseph was back, and the kids were not going into care, it seemed trivial.

When Joseph eventually arrived, he was angry and upset. The police offered to drive Joseph home again with the children. I hugged Joseph and the children. They waved to me and a wave of despair came over me, as I knew I was to be separated from them.

It was after one in the morning when the social worker arrived. I answered the same questions as the Police Dr had asked me. I did my best to reassure that at no stage was I going to harm my children, that all I was doing was trying to stop them being taken into care. The social worker smiled, "Actually, all the police have said was how well you cared for them, making sure they didn't hurt themselves or get cold." I smiled back.

It was nearly half past two in the morning, when the Inspector and the police woman took me back to the ward. Melanie was on duty and gave me a warm welcome. They had my old room waiting and a new nurse called Susan was to stay with me. She was nice, extremely attractive with long blonde hair and a slender figure. I thanked the police. Melanie and Susan invited me into the nurses station for a cup of tea, I sat up a while answering their questions. Some time later, I went to bed, Susan sat by the bed. I was on level ones. I fell asleep.

In the morning when Dr Lynn came, he was accompanied by another nurse I liked called Helen. She was tall and slim, short hair, lovely eyes and had a kind *smile. We were of similar age. She was the nurse who had introduced me to the Harry Potter books in the past. "What do you want us to do about last night?" Dr Lynn asked.*

"Forget about it," I replied quickly. They both laughed.

Dr Lynn came and sat in the chair next to me. "Do you realise how serious it was last night? You had half the police force out, looking for you." I stared at him, as I tried to protest, he continued. "I want to put you on some medication; I want you to take an antipsychotic drug."

I looked at him in amazement and shook my head, "No way, I am not psychotic." I stared at Helen; she tried to back him up.

"We are only going to give you the lowest dose, it might stop the bad thoughts you get." Again, I looked at her and then him, and I again shook my head. "Well, you are going to be in here for an awful long time if you don't take it," Dr Lynn spoke. I again shook my head adamantly. He continued, "I am away for the next week or so, I'll see you when I get back." I stood up as he was making his way out, and dashed to stand in front of him. "I don't want to be here, how do I get out? I don't want to wait for you to get back."

"Well take the medication then," he smiled and walked off. Helen followed him and an agency nurse was beckoned to sit with me. I felt frustrated and not at all calm. There was no way I wanted a chemical straightjacket. I sat back on the bed and rang Joseph up. He was as alarmed as I was, "Don't take it," he said.

As I continued to write, I felt sick as of all my memories this part was one of the most traumatic and it still made me feel ill.

For the next two weeks the nurses did their best to try to persuade me to take the drug, each time I refused I was reminded that I was the one not seeing my family, and stuck in the hospital.

Dr Lynn was still away. I had to see the other consultant Dr Libber again the next day. I was worried as some of the nurses had hinted that if I did not comply, I would be held down whilst they injected me. They were entitled to do this as I was sectioned.

I had witnessed this happen several times to an unfortunate patient and it was a degrading event, as sometimes it was done openly on the ward and not in the privacy of a room.

The night before I was due to see Dr Libber, I had been told I would be injected if I did not agree. I did not think Dr Lynn would order it to happen, but I did not know Dr Libber that well, and I decided after a lot of persuasion to take the drug. I swallowed the pill and went to bed.

In the morning when I woke up, I felt awful I could not keep my eyes open and I felt faint. I made my way over the corridor into the toilet. I sat on it quick as I thought I was going to collapse, and I did black out, toppling off into the sink. It was only shortly and I opened my eyes to the grim sight of the toilet floor, I dragged myself up clinging on to the sink, and splashed my face with cold water. I opened the door and gingerly made my way over to my bed. I collapsed onto it. I did not want to know anything, I felt so ill. The next few weeks were to be of a similar pattern, the drug hit so hard I could not keep awake in the morning. I lost some of the afternoon also.

I was worried how I would cope at home when I could not wake up in the morning. Dr Lynn kept telling me it would wear off. It did not. My nose dried up so bad, it was uncomfortable, my periods stopped and I kept having spasms on my tongue that I could not control. I tried my best to be compliant, as I needed to get out.

It was heading towards the summer and they decided I could go home. Andrea and Dr Lynn kept telling me how much better I was. The people who knew me and saw me daily had a completely different opinion. I was at Denny's house, and Mum was there with Jane and Richard. Joseph sat at the table outside with me, our two children were playing with their cousins in the garden. Mum, Jane and Denny were in the kitchen behind me washing up. I could not be bothered to move, I sat there in the sun partly aware of a conversation between Richard and Joseph. I could not be bothered to take part.

Denny rang me up later, she said they were all worried about me as it was as if I was there, but I was not.

It was a few weeks later, when Paula my home start lady who had become like another Mum and friend, and did have a son called Dylan, dropped round unexpectedly with her daughter. She was a nice girl called Lisa. Joseph offered them a drink and I smiled politely. Paula spoke to me and Lisa sat outside with me. Then they called the children out to give Tee Jay his birthday present.

It was during that week that I had a long hard think. Paula rang me later and told me Lisa was so shocked, she said I was not the person she had met before, it was as if I was empty. Paula continued, "I'm worried about you, Bridge; they have put a chemical straight jacket on you. You might be safe but you have no life, it makes me cross, it's an easy way out for them." Later I spoke to Joseph, "I've decided, I respected Dr Lynn, I did what he asked, I tried the drug out and I have been on it for six months, but it's not helped. It has made me safe, but I have no life. It has stopped the bad thoughts, but it has taken away all thoughts. It has dampened down the impulsiveness yet it has taken away any motivation or life. I want to stop it. I would rather have a life with risks, than no life at all," I hesitated and looked at Joseph. He was nodding in agreement.

CHAPTER 17

Trust

Dr Lynn and Andrea disagreed that I was better off the medication, and we agreed to disagree. They only saw me for a brief period at a time. The people who lived with me were certain I was better off it. I remained adamant that I wanted a life and refused to consider it again.

Dr Lynn understood that although to many people, my life looked normal, I would have to avoid certain situations. He tried to introduce me to some of his Junior Dr's and Senior Registrars, to try to show me that I could trust other people. I could still bolt in enclosed rooms or with people I did not know, so I was very wary.

The Senior Registrar who I was seeing at the time was lovely. He was from New Zealand, having a fantastic attitude and a good insight to my problems. He was very open and honest and I felt lucky to have his support. He was eventually returning to New Zealand, once he qualified as a consultant. He made me promise that one day, when I had finished the book I wanted to write, he could have a copy. He had asked me what sort of book I wanted to write, I had said I wanted to do an autobiography, but not directly about me, I half said this, as I still had to distance from it. I continued, "I want this book to help other people who might have been in a similar situation," he was nodding. "Explain," he said.

"If people were in the same situation, I never recognised what was happening, someone reading this might recognise they have problems and also I'd like some help phone numbers in the back, there are so many more help lines available now than when I was young. I also want it to be a good book to read." He laughed, "Well I definitely want a copy."

"Do you know what else would be a good idea?" I shook my head wondering what he was going to say. "If you could write a book, just on your feelings on your illness and views of how you are being treated professionally, I know I'd read that, and there is a shortage of insight to patient's views." He leant back on his chair, scribbling some notes down. I continued our conversation eagerly, "Yes, I have just achieved a distinction in Health and Social Care, and one of the issues, is that people have more say in their care, if I have time after, I could consider that. Dr Lynn suggested I did a report once as a patient on the care at the ward. I didn't have time."

He laughed, "You never have time with all those animals, and I'm surprised you haven't any sheep." This time I laughed. I could imagine him shearing sheep looking at him, with his suede shoes, smart jeans, and check shirt.

I said, "Only a true New Zealander could say that," we both were laughing as we left the room. I would be sorry when he moved. I just hoped he would qualify and be as good as Dr Lynn had been to me.

After him, I saw another Senior Registrar who I nicknamed Pingu, after a penguin my children liked. He was nice and so full of respect for me he boosted my self-esteem. Another Dr saw me for 6 months after him and again, I started to feel that maybe there were some good people in the world.

CHAPTER 18

Resolution

Slowly the years passed by, I managed to stay out of hospital relying on weekly visits there, and fortnightly visits to Dr Rosa my GP whom I know had a brilliant repertoire. She was so professional, I felt I could relax and tell her absolutely anything, some weeks we had a good laugh, and I felt relieved that I had some great support there. She often had to advise me on my physical problems, although I had been told I had posttraumatic stress disorder, Dr Lynn had said my diagnosis was complex and included various symptoms of other diagnosis labels. These often led to psychosomatic symptoms, my Meniere's disease could be related to stress, so could my ME and migraines. I used to joke that I took the three S's, which was my medication for the three M's, which my illnesses were. I also had IBS, which again related to stress. Dr Rosa was good and she helped me manage my physical symptoms, as well as supporting me on my mental well-being. I felt extremely sensitive to life. My philosophy was every life was as important as any other was. Politics and religion destroyed nations and innocent people.

Slowly I started to trust some people and open up a tiny bit more. My house started to feel like a home instead of a base. My real Mum I name my biological Mum, as my real Mum is my adoptive Mum. I miss my Dad who lost his battle to pancreatic cancer, and although nearly ten years on, my love for him is as strong as ever. I also miss both my Nan's and felt lucky to have known both.

My life has started to piece back together. I still love my Mum to bits, and Denny and Jane; they have aged with me, both separating from their husbands. The children's school life has brought many friends into our family. I have some close friends that I would have not believed possible years ago. Paula is still a brilliant friend, and support to the whole family. I don't know how the clairvoyant knew, but she had told me I would meet a lady in her fifties, who would be blonde and have a son named Dylan and become a good friend. She had told me at the time I would not meet the lady until a few years later. I have no explanation but Paula fitted the description exactly.

Joseph and I are travelling on a rollercoaster life. Joseph's wine business is established and he is supporting me writing this book. He will be one of the first people to read it. Tee Jay and Jo Jo are growing up fast, and I am now trying to provide the security and stability they had lost in their earlier lives.

Dr Lynn is still seeing me fortnightly, and I believe I am extremely fortunate to have him as my consultant. We still argue and laugh, but are able to liaise at a high professional level that has grown with experience. My New Zealander is now living in New Zealand, as a consultant and waiting for this book. I hope that I will be able to track him to send it.

Although I have to go to the hospital regularly, I now see nurses who come up to me and give me a hug as friends not foes. Anna ran over to embrace me this week, I had not seen her for years. Dr Lynn's secretary gave me a hug last week her words, "You're looking as beautiful as ever," not bad from a friendly dragon, who I used to be scared of. Yesterday at hospital, I saw Andrea, we stopped and looked at each other and embraced like long lost friends. We have each matured up our own pathways and still have mutual respect for each other.

My life has had many extremities, yet these extremities have opened up new doors and I have learnt a great deal of experience, respect, and insight through them.

As I travel along my very fine line, I have come to realise that I do have friends, family and some of the finest support available, and one day my very fine line may broaden to a platform.

NHS Direct Healthcare concerns. Phone 0845 46 47(24 hour service)

NSPCC Children's charity dedicated to ending child abuse and child cruelty.Phone:0800 1111 for Childline for children. 0808 800 5000 for adults concerned about a child. Website: www.nspcc.org.uk

Refuge Advice on dealing with domestic violence.Phone: 0808 2000 247 Website: www.refuge.org.uk

Samaritans Confidential support for people experiencing feelings of distress or despair. Phone: 08457 90 90 90 (24-hour helpline) Website: www.samaritans.org.uk

Sane Charity support and carrying out research into mental illness. Phone: 0845 767 8000 (daily, 1pm-11pm) email: sanemail@org.uk Website: www.sane.org.uk

The Rape and Abuse Line (RAL) A registered charity that offers a freephone, confidential helpline to persons who have survived rape or abuse however long ago the experiences were. Helpline: 0808 800 0123 answered by women. Helpline:0808 800 0122 answered by men. Office: 01349 865316

www.Mind.org.uk A charity for supporting mental health issues. Infoline 0845 766 0163.

My Website www.afineline-lisawb.co.uk will be a website for information on mental health issues, advice on where to get help, and a site where further information about the book will be available.

Joseph's Website www.amphora-wines.co.uk is Joseph's website. It is his site for giving information on many quality wines and the availability of the one's he has for sale. It also gives information on his wine tastings and location of his shop.

Gifteasy Website www.bronzeharesculptures.com. This site is one set up recently to sell quality gifts at a decent price, and it has been the result of following up requests from regular customers.

ACKNOWLEDGEMENTS

My thanks go to my family for their support, my friends, who know who they are, and I hope they value me as much as I value them.

My acknowledgement could not miss out my pet's who I love dearly and have given me masses of unconditional love and support.

I am impressed at the professionalism and fantastic support from all the staff at Troubador Publishing, and thanks to Ed Fenton at Writer's Workshop for his motivation and expertise.

An appreciative thanks goes to all the medical professionals, especially my consultant, and I would like to acknowledge Dr Louisa who although has only just stepped into my life, and unfortunately has to move on, will be remembered as a very dedicated GP.

I would like to mention a special tribute to all those who have survived any aspect of trauma, and especially those brave enough to write about their experience to allow access to valuable insights to their experiences.

Last but not least, I would also like to thank any reader's of this book, and hope that the more awareness raised will help people recognise the symptoms of child abuse, and realise that although child abuse is an ongoing concern, it is people like the general public who can step in and may make a difference.